WESTMAR COLLEGE

American
Sculpture

A CATALOGUE OF THE COLLECTION OF THE METROPOLITAN MUSEUM OF ART

American Sculpture

A CATALOGUE OF THE COLLECTION OF
THE METROPOLITAN MUSEUM OF ART

Albert TenEyck Gardner

*Late Associate Curator of American Paintings
and Sculpture*

The Metropolitan Museum of Art

Distributed by New York Graphic Society Ltd., Greenwich, Connecticut

Contents

Introduction

THE AMERICAN SCULPTURE in the Metropolitan Museum, gathered by gift and by purchase over a long period of years—almost a century, in fact—provides a fairly complete record of the art of sculpture in this country. In certain respects it affords as good a survey of what has been going on in the world of American sculpture as can be found anywhere.

The collection now numbers 354 pieces of sculpture, the work of 176 native-born or adopted citizens of the United States. This aggregation, so large and so varied, the work of so many hands, composed as it is of sculpture ranging in scale from heroic groups to miniature cabinet bronzes and in style from the Italianate neoclassic of the early nineteenth century to the abstract manner of today, naturally includes work that aimed at, but never quite attained, the permanent status of great works of art. In the main, however, it contains a good number of substantial examples that have found their places in the history of American sculpture. Many earlier pieces are of sufficiently high quality to have at one time seemed to be masterpieces, but some of them have not managed in the slow passage of time, or in the face of swift changes in taste and critical temper, to remain fixed in that extremely small category. Much of the sculpture of the nineteenth century has a strong memorial, literary, or historical cast. The passage of a mere fifty years (or even less) can, and often does, demote a grand sculptural ornament into a historical curio. But time also works the other way, turning what once were considered historical curios into first-class cultural monuments.

The first piece of American sculpture, and one of the first works by an American artist, to enter the Museum's collection was the marble statue California by Hiram Powers, presented by William B. Astor in 1872. It is the cornerstone, so to speak, of our collection of American art. Viewed as a whole, the collection falls into three distinct though unequal groups. First there are the marbles made by early nineteenth-century sculptors who, like Powers, went to study and live in Italy; second, the largest of the three groups, the bronzes made by those of a later generation who studied in Paris in the last decades of the nineteenth century; and, third, the work of contemporary sculptors. It may be said that most of the sculpture in the collection was made in the fifty-year period between 1870 and 1920 by men and women trained in Paris under the masters of the École des Beaux Arts. As the tastes and sculptural ideas of those masters were formed during the heyday of the Second Empire of Napoleon III, they admitted no higher honor than the medals and "Honorable Mentions" awarded at the annual

Paris Salon. This standard was readily accepted by the majority of their American pupils, and between 1855 and 1914 no less than a hundred and sixty American sculptors won the coveted privilege of showing their work at the Salon. More than thirty pieces of sculpture now in the Museum's collection were first exhibited there. Some of these succeeded so well with the jury that they received the dazzling accolade of "Honorable Mention," and one or two received the higher honors of a Medal of the Second or Third Class.

Of the nine works now in the Museum that were first exhibited in the Salon and there accorded an Honorable Mention, some retain a certain amount of interest; others are not now well remembered: Salon of 1880, Statue of Farragut by Saint-Gaudens; 1886, The Young Sophocles by John Donoghue; 1887, The Bohemian Bear-Tamer by Paul Bartlett; 1888, Evening by F. Wellington Ruckstull; 1889, Diana by Frederick MacMonnies; 1890, The Bather by Edmund Stewardson; 1895, The Song of the Wave by Richard Brooks and the Tomb Effigy of Elizabeth Boott Duveneck by Frank Duveneck; 1913, the Arlington Fountain by Gertrude V. Whitney.

In collecting data for a survey certain facts become apparent that cast new light on the collection. For instance, most sculptors are represented by only one or two examples of their work, yet there are several who are represented by numerous pieces. Strangely enough, one of the largest groups by a single artist is the work of a now relatively obscure man, Olin Warner, whose friends claimed that his portrait busts rivaled those of the Greeks—an opinion now incomprehensible. Another large collection of bronzes by one sculptor is the group of nineteen pieces by Augustus Saint-Gaudens, who for many years held a sort of semi-official position in the American art world as "the greatest American sculptor." Still another large group is the work of the illustrator Frederic Remington. Interest in his work has been sustained by the widespread enthusiasm for his Wild West subject matter—cowboys and Indians. Other sculptors represented by three or more works include Frederick MacMonnies, Paul Bartlett, Paul Manship, Malvina Hoffman, Anna Vaughn Hyatt Huntington, Evelyn Longman, Gaston Lachaise, Charles Calverley, Daniel Chester French, Bessie Potter Vonnoh, John Quincy Adams Ward, Thomas Crawford, Hiram Powers, William Rimmer, William Rinehart, William Story, Launt Thompson, and Herbert Haseltine.

An analysis of the collection by subject matter throws a sidelight on the kinds of things that interested sculptors and their patrons. It is natural, significant, and not surprising to discover that one of the most interesting things in sculpture is human beings, and that about one third of the collection consists of portraits. There are well over a hundred of them, the majority studied from living persons. Two thirds of the portraits are of men. There are thirteen of artists and a great number of all sorts of political, social, and historical personages, ranging among the women from Susan B.

Anthony to Anna Pavlova, among the men from George Washington to Elihu Root, from Henry Ward Beecher to Jules S. Bache. There are some prominent old New Yorkers: Mary de Peyster, John Watts, Marshall O. Roberts, J. Insley Blair, and William Tilden Blodgett, one of the Founders of this Museum. There are naturally more portraits of Abraham Lincoln (four of them) than anyone else. Of Civil War heroes we have Generals Sherman and Hancock, Major General Philip Kearny, and Admiral Farragut. In this group of portraits we find the most important historical document and one of the best portraits, Hiram Powers' bust of President Andrew Jackson, made from life studies modeled in the White House in 1835. The largest portrait is a bronze bust in heroic scale of William Cullen Bryant by Launt Thompson, which has remained a storeroom stumbling block since 1896, when it was deposited in the Museum as a "temporary" loan from the Department of Parks. The smallest portrait is a tiny statuette of Pavlova by Alfred Lenz, famous for his minute castings in precious metals; here sculpture seems to approach the personal scale of jewelry.

The other large group of subjects is that of animals, again about a third of the collection, with the horse the natural winner of the animal sweepstakes. Many of the animal sculptures are small bronzes; fortunately none of the horses are life size.

The most imposing monumental group in the collection, a romantic sculptural *tour de force* colossal in size, is the strange and powerful Struggle of the Two Natures in Man by George Grey Barnard.

In the past fifteen or twenty years the collection has been enlivened by the addition of a number of works by contemporary sculptors, most of whom have abandoned the white marble and bronze of their predecessors for free experimentation with all sorts of modern materials. Here we find sculpture considered in new ways in the search for significant forms and new feelings for plastic and glyptic modes undreamed of by Powers or Saint-Gaudens.

The Museum's collection of American sculpture represents the choice and judgment of many men. In the early days before there were funds for purchasing works of art, all gifts of sculpture were examined and approved by the sculptor John Quincy Adams Ward, one of the Founders and a Trustee of the Museum. At first the small American collection was not separated from other modern sculpture. From 1885 to 1896 all sculpture was under the care of a Curator of Sculpture, Professor Isaac H. Hall. His domain, in fact, included all works of art except paintings. Professor Hall was a Biblical scholar, a specialist in Syriac languages whose main interest was in the archaeology of the Holy Land. On the death of Professor Hall, William R. Arnold was made Curator. He remained in office only two years. After his departure the position remained vacant until 1903, when the sculptor Edwin Elwell was appointed Curator of Ancient and Modern Statuary. Elwell was employed to restore and repair the Greco

Roman marbles in the classical collection, and on the completion of this work in¯1905 he left the Museum. From then until 1931, the modern sculpture collection was supervised by the sculptor Daniel Chester French, who had been elected a Trustee of the Museum in 1903. The greater part of the sculpture now in the collection was acquired during his incumbency of twenty-six years as Chairman of the Trustees' Committee on Sculpture; thus the greater part of the collection reflects his tastes and enthusiasms. On the death of French in 1931, the modern sculpture collection was placed in the charge of the Curator of Renaissance and Modern Art. In 1941 it was separated from this department and placed under the jurisdiction of Horace H. F. Jayne, then Vice-Director. In 1949 the collection was divided, and the modern European sculpture reverted to the Department of Renaissance and Modern Art, while the American sculpture was placed under the care of the then newly formed Department of American Art.

ALBERT TenEYCK GARDNER

American
Sculpture

A CATALOGUE OF THE COLLECTION OF THE METROPOLITAN MUSEUM OF ART

NOTE: The biographies in the catalogue are, in general, brief. Detailed biographies, including much unpublished material from the Museum's files, are given for those sculptors whose stories are not easily found in the standard reference works. Only basic information is given for living sculptors.

59.89

Unknown Sculptor

American Eagle   59.89

This emblem of the United States, probably made sometime between 1800 and 1830, is said to have come from the vicinity of Phila- delphia. It is possibly the work of a carver of ship figureheads, although it does not appear to have been used as a ship ornament, nor on the outside of a building, as it shows no sign of weathering.

Wood, gilded, height 62 in.

PURCHASE, ELLA MORRIS DE PEYSTER FUND, 1959.

Horatio Greenough

1805–1852

BORN in Boston; died in Somerville, Massa- chusetts. Greenough began his career by copy- ing plaster casts in the Boston Athenaeum.

After graduating from Harvard in 1824, he went to Italy to continue studying sculpture, especially marble-carving at the Carrara quar- ries.

When he settled in Florence he met and became a close friend of James Fenimore Cooper, who constantly encouraged him and later gave him his first major commission, The Chanting Cherubs. This work was much praised in Boston by Washington Allston, also a close friend and admirer. It was Allston who brought Greenough to the attention of Daniel Webster when Congress was consider- ing ordering a statue of George Washington for the Capitol. The commission for this statue, received in 1832, made Greenough the first American artist to be given an im- portant assignment by the government.

In 1842 Greenough came to the United States to supervise the installation of his statue of Washington, but returned to Italy in 1843. In 1851 he decided to settle perma- nently in Somerville, Massachusetts, where he died the following year from an attack of "brain fever."

Horatio Greenough is remembered today not so much for his sculpture as for his writings on art. Perhaps his most original thought is summed up in "The Stonecutter's Creed," for these three simple sentences contain the seeds of the modern theory of functionalism, which has in recent years been so important in the development of modern design, particularly in the field of modern architecture. Greenough wrote: "By beauty I mean the promise of function. By action I mean the presence of function. By character I mean the record of function." Renewed interest in Greenough's ideas has resulted in the republication of his essays on art.

Samuel Finley Breese Morse   x . 331

Bust of Samuel F. B. Morse (1791–1872), the founder of the National Academy of Design (1825), inventor of the Morse telegraph and Morse code, and a Founder of The Metropolitan Museum of Art. This bust was made about 1832; the original marble formerly in the Council Chamber of the National Academy of Design was commissioned in 1841.

Painted plaster, height 21½ in.

x. 331

EXHIBITED: National Academy of Design, New York, 1833 (marble).

SOURCE UNKNOWN.

Hiram Powers

1805–1873

BORN in Woodstock, Vermont; died in Florence. As a youth in Cincinnati, where his family had moved, Powers showed marked inventive and mechanical ability. He began his work in sculpture by modeling figures for a waxworks museum. In 1834 he went to Washington, where he executed several portrait busts, and in 1837 his Cincinnati patron, Nicholas Longworth, paid for a trip to Italy for him. Powers remained in Florence for the rest of his life, turning out portrait busts and a few ideal figures. The most famous of these was the Greek Slave (1843), which won him an international reputation when it was exhibited at the Crystal Palace Exhibition in London in 1851. Today this figure appears as a cultural curio. All of Powers' work, with the possible exception of his portrait busts made in this country before he went to stay in Italy, was strongly influenced by the work of the Italian followers of Canova and the Danish sculptor Thorwaldsen, whose flattering comments on Powers' early works were influential in establishing his extraordinary reputation. Powers was elected an honorary member of the National Academy of Design in 1838 and exhibited portrait busts at the Academy in 1843 and 1853. He was perhaps the most famous American sculptor of his day, though time has now shorn him of almost all the glittering qualities attributed to him by his many friends.

President Andrew Jackson   94.14

Andrew Jackson (1767–1845), seventh president of the United States (1829–1836). The sculptor reported that when he was modeling this bust he asked the President if he wished

his portrait to be idealized—the wrinkles smoothed, the mouth rejuvenated. Jackson exclaimed, "Make me as I am, Mr. Powers, and be true to nature always. . . . I have no desire to look young as long as I feel old; and then it seems to me, although I don't know much about sculpture, that the only object in making a bust is to get a representation of the man who sits, that it be as nearly as possible a perfect likeness."

Jackson is represented at the age of sixty-eight. His shoulders are draped in a Roman toga, the costume prescribed by the neoclassic style for all portraits of statesmen. The original clay study for this head was made by Powers at the beginning of his career, in 1835, at the White House. When the young sculptor arrived in Italy in 1837, one of his first projects was to carve this bust in marble. It is one of the few works by Powers that is known to have been carved in the stone entirely by his hand; the general practice of the time was to have this work done by professional Italian marble-cutters. Thus it derives its vigorous personal quality directly from the sculptor. Powers here achieved a striking combination of dignity, force, and fidelity that is seldom to be found in his later works. Its historic importance as a faithful portrait from life places it well above Powers' other portraits. Its sculptural qualities eclipse his notorious Greek Slave and his other "fancy pieces." The Jackson bust may be considered as Powers' best work. It may even be said to epitomize all that is best in the American portrait sculpture of the period, just as his Greek Slave seems to embody all that is meretricious.

Sheldon I. Kellogg, an artist visiting the White House in 1835, wrote, "I saw the plaster model of this bust . . . standing on a side table . . . and the Hero President by its side, and scrutinizing both critically, I can say it is a remarkable likeness of the Great Man."

In spite of many offers, Powers kept this bust in his studio in Florence until after the death of Jackson; it was then sold, in 1846, to a Democratic Club in New York City for a sum reputed to be $2500. In 1874 it was lent to the Museum for its first exhibition of mod-

ern sculpture. The original plaster was reported in 1949 to be still in the possession of Powers' descendants in Florence. This bust was to be the first of a series, planned by Powers, of marble portraits of all the presidents, to be placed in the Capitol in Washington.

Marble, height 34½ in. Signed: Hiram Powers Sculp.

REFERENCES: C. E. Lester, *The Artist, the Merchant and the Statesman* (1845); H. W. Bellows, "Seven Sittings with Powers the Sculptor," *Appleton's Journal*, 1 (1869):342; S. I. Kellogg, letter in the Museum archives (1883); *Catalogue of Sculpture* (Metropolitan Museum, 1908); A. T. Gardner, *Met. Mus. Bull.*, new series 2 (1943):102; A. T. Gardner, *Yankee Stonecutters* (1945), pp. 29 f.

EXHIBITED: Metropolitan Museum, 1874–1883; Cincinnati Art Museum, 1888.

EX COLL.: H. Powers, Florence (1837–1846); Democratic Club, New York (1846?–1849?); Sheldon I. Kellogg, New York (1849–1883?).

GIFT OF MRS. FRANCES V. NASH, 1894.

The Fisher Boy   94.9.1

In a letter preserved in the archives of the Cincinnati Museum Association Powers described this work: "A boy of eight or nine years, standing with a conch shell to his ear, listening, with upturned face expressive of disappointment, while in his right hand he holds a net and tiller. To denote the seabeach on which he stands, there will be at his feet, half buried in the sand, some shells and seaweed, and the whole relates to the notion entertained by many on the borders of the ocean, that a storm may be foretold by the increased roar from within the conch shell. This statue should realize about $2000." In one of his conversations with C. Edwards Lester, Powers described this figure as follows: "I had modeled a little figure which I called the Fisher Boy. It is a difficult thing to find a subject of modern times whose history and peculiarities will justify entire nudity. . . .

This figure is a kind of Apollino, but the character is modern; for I hold that artists should do honor to their own times and their own religion instead of going back to mythology to illustrate, for the thousandth time, the incongruous absurdities and inconsistencies of idolatrous times, especially as our times and our religion are full of subjects equal in beauty, and have all the qualities necessary to a full development of art."

The shell the boy holds was copied from one borrowed from the Grand Ducal Cabinet in Florence. Powers had made a very pleasing portrait bust of the Grand Duchess, who also allowed him to take a plaster cast from the original Venus de' Medici. This cast later formed the basis of all Powers' statues of nude women.

Marble, height 57 in. Signed: H. Powers Sculp. Dated 1848.

REPLICAS: Private collection, Cincinnati, 1934 (head only); private collection, Newport, Rhode Island, 1934; private collection, Florence, 1934.

REFERENCES: H. Powers, letter to Mr. Lea, 1841, archives of the Cincinnati Art Association; *The Art Union*, 9 (1847):110; *Catalogue of Sculpture* (Metropolitan Museum, 1908).

BEQUEST OF HAMILTON FISH, 1894.

California 72.3

This figure, which Powers originally called La Dorado, was designed in Florence in 1850. It enjoys the distinction of being the first work by an American artist to become part of the collections of this Museum. It was purchased from the artist in 1858 by William Backhouse Astor (who is said to have paid $7500 for it), and from 1858 until it entered the Museum's collection it was one of the principal ornaments of Mr. Astor's New York residence in Astor Place. Perhaps the Museum owes the gift of this figure as much to some remarks about it published in Tuckerman's *Book of the Artists* as to the change in taste of its owner. It was presented to the Museum

after Mrs. Astor's death when Mr. Astor moved uptown to a new house at Fifth Avenue and Thirty-fourth Street. Tuckerman wrote, "At a brilliant party given by its owner this work was the nucleus of a gay crowd; it

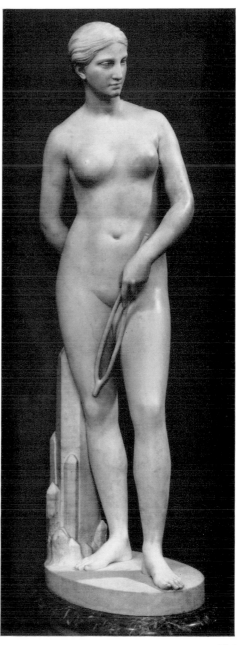

72.3

even drew attention from the many speci-
mens of living beauty around, and the exquisite flowers and toilettes were comparatively neglected. Evidently the sculptor's idea
is to contrast the fascination of form with the
sinister expression of the face,—the thorn con-
cealed in the left hand with the divining rod
displayed in the right,—and thus illustrate
the deceitfulness of riches. It is a singular coin-
cidence that such an allegorical statue should
adorn the dwelling of our wealthiest citizen."
(Tuckerman's description placed thorns and
divining rod in the wrong hands.) In its awk-
wardly arranged pose and symbolic accessories
—thorns, divining rod, and quartz crystals—
it shares the general character of its more famous sister, the Greek Slave. Hawthorne also
mentions this work in his *Italian Notebooks*.
The original plaster model of the head is in a
private collection in Florence.

Marble, height 71 in. Inscribed: Executed for
W. B. Astor by Hiram Powers April 3d 1858.

REPLICAS: Private collection, Florence, 1934
(head only); M. H. de Young Memorial
Museum, San Francisco (head only).

REFERENCES: J. Powers, letter in *The Literary
World*, 8 (1851):237; H. T. Tuckerman, *Book
of the Artists* (1870); N. Hawthorne, *Italian
Notebooks* (1871); *Catalogue of Sculpture*
(Metropolitan Museum, 1908); A. T. Gard-
ner, "A Relic of the California Gold Rush,"
Met Mus. Bull., new series 8 (1949):117.

GIFT OF WILLIAM BACKHOUSE ASTOR, 1872.

Ball Hughes

1806–1868

Robert Ball Hughes. Born in London; died
in Dorchester, Massachusetts. Hughes was a
student at the Royal Academy School and a
pupil of Edward H. Baily, in whose studio he
absorbed the neoclassic manner of Flaxman.
His work was shown in the Royal Academy
exhibitions in 1822, 1824, 1825, and 1828.
When he came to the United States about
1829 he had already won some fame by his

portrait busts and statuettes of the Prince
Regent. For several years he remained in
New York, where he was patronized by the
aristocracy. In 1831 he was elected an Hon-
orary Member of the National Academy of
Design. About 1842 he settled in Dorchester,
Massachusetts, where he remained for the rest
of his life.

Hughes's work was largely confined to portraits, busts, statuettes, and wax miniatures.
His marble statue of Alexander Hamilton,
made for the rotunda of the New York Merchants' Exchange, was destroyed by fire a few
months after it was unveiled in 1835. His
monument to Nathaniel Bowditch (1847),
a bronze portrait statue in Mount Auburn
Cemetery, Cambridge, was later modified by
recasting in Paris in the 1880's. These two
works have been singled out by some historians as the first marble statue and the first
bronze statue to be made in the United States,
and as such they have enjoyed a certain prominence. Perhaps the best existing work by
Hughes is the rather pompous and "official"
portrait bust of John Trumbull in the Yale
Art Gallery.

Hughes's career in this country was unhap-
pily marred by the ignominious failure of two
projects in which he became involved. He was
commissioned to restore the burned fragments
of Canova's Washington, destroyed by fire in
Raleigh, North Carolina, in 1831. Some accounts say that he accepted payment in ad-
vance but never appeared in Raleigh to carry
out his contract. In 1841 he was commissioned
to make a statue of Washington for the City
of Philadelphia; this project was brought to
an abrupt termination by the failure of the
Bank of the United States in that year. From
this time on he was occupied largely with the
minor art of modeling wax profile portraits,
the trivialities of the dubious art of pyrog-
raphy, and giving lectures in Boston on the
wonders of sculpture.

Two letters in the Museum's Archives
throw some light on his career. One, from his
wife, is, naturally, adulatory in tone; the other,
from an irate patron, is perhaps quite as preju-
diced though from an entirely different cause.

The letter from Mrs. Ball Hughes is undated but was probably written to E. D. Adams about 1880:

"Dear Sir:

In reply to your letter just received. I do not think that any artist ever attempted burning on wood (except one talented boy who is now in Europe studying—his name was Fosdyke). The whole thing was done as a joke by my husband who going into the kitchen and finding a clean clapboard which someone had brought in; Took it up and having put the poker in the fire till it was red hot, burnt the head of one of Fuseli's Witches and then left it on the parlor table—it created quite a sensation, . . .

And he has burnt from Landseer, Gilbert, Goodall and these pokerisms have fetch'd at auction as high as $400 and I heard of one going to be sold for 500 dollars. . . .

I have the *original* or first he burnt and two other small pictures—but they do not compare with those in which he did wonders! Mr. Hughes profession was that of a sculptor and these were merely pastime amusements. . . .

I have loved to talk of him hence all this detail, and I wish you to remember him as a sculptor of great talent indeed a man of genius —which show'd itself in whatever he touch'd.

I remain, Dear Sir, Yours Respectfully
E. Ball Hughes"

The second letter is from John Watts de Peyster. It reads in part: ". . . please let your wagon deliver my plaster bust of John Watts in safety to my city residence. . . . Please, I earnestly beg of you let your man take the best care of the plaster bust which is an original by Ball Hughes an eminent artist but a vagabond, like so many artists, because he carried off two portraits of my ancestors . . . and they could never be recovered."

John Watts   06.982

This bronze bust of John Watts (1749–1836), a prominent citizen of New York, was cast between 1900 and 1906 for presentation to the Museum.

A memorial statue of Watts by George Bissell in Trinity Church Graveyard bears the following inscription, which illuminates his career:

"Vir Aequanimitatis. John Watts. Born in the City of New York, August 27, 1749 and died there September 3, 1836. Last Royal Recorder of the City of New York 1774–1777; No Records During the Revolution; Speaker of the Assembly of the State of New York 1791– 1794; Member of Congress 1793–1795; First Judge of Westchester County 1806; Founder and Endower of the Leake and Watts Orphan House in the City of New York; One of the Founders and afterwards President of the New York Dispensary 1821–1836 etc. etc."

The original plaster bust of Watts by Hughes was in City Hall until 1945 when it was smashed by a vandal.

Bronze, height 26½ in. Signed: Hughes (partly obliterated). Founder's mark: Gruet jne. Fondeurs, Paris.

REPLICA: New-York Historical Society, New York (copy by Thomas Coffee).

REFERENCES: Frank Allaben, *John Watts de Peyster* (1906) (contains genealogical details about the subject of the bust and the donor); *Catalogue of Sculpture* (Metropolitan Museum, 1908).

GIFT OF GENERAL JOHN WATTS DE PEYSTER, 1906.

Joel Tanner Hart

1810–1877

BORN in Winchester, Kentucky; died in Florence. As a youth Hart was apprenticed to a stonecutter. At the age of twenty-one he met the young sculptor Shobal Vail Clevenger (see p. 9), who was then in Lexington, Kentucky, modeling a portrait of Henry Clay. Hart's interest in sculpture and also his interest in Henry Clay as a sculptural subject date from this time. After gaining some local fame as a maker of portrait busts, Hart was commissioned in 1846 by the Richmond Ladies' Clay Association to make a statue of their hero Henry Clay. This commission occupied the sculptor for thirteen years. When the statue was completed and erected in Richmond, the great popularity of Henry Clay (rather than the quality of the sculpture) prompted two other Southern cities to order replicas to be made by Hart at ten thousand dollars each. These three very lucrative commissions enabled Hart to live in Florence for the rest of his life. During his lifetime he was noted as the inventor of an elaborate machine for making copies of portrait busts. Some years after his death his body was exhumed and shipped to Kentucky, where it was reinterred with great ceremony in the State Cemetery at Frankfort.

Henry Clay   95.2.6

Attributed to Hart. This cabinet bust of the American statesman and orator Henry Clay (1777–1852), though of no great significance

as a work of art, has several points of interest. For a brief period, from about 1840 to 1850, it was fashionable to have small portraits made in marble to distribute among one's friends as mementos. A number of young American sculptors undertook work of this sort at the beginning of their careers, turning out these small portraits for about twenty-five dollars each. This particular cabinet bust was presented by Clay to Miss Anne Charlotte Lynch (later Mrs. Botta), who was long a prominent figure in literary and artistic circles in New York.

Marble, height 6 in.

REFERENCES: V. Botta, *Last Will and Testament of Vincenzo Botta*; V. Botta, *Memoirs of Anne Charlotte Lynch Botta* (1894); A. T. Gardner, "The Arts and Mrs. Botta," *Met. Mus. Bull.*, new series 6 (1947):105.

EX COLL.: Anne Charlotte Lynch Botta, New York.

BEQUEST OF VINCENZO BOTTA, 1895.

95.2.6

Chauncey Bradley Ives

1810–1894

BORN in Hamden, Connecticut; died in Rome. Ives received his early training with the wood-carvers Hezekiah Augur and Northrup but did not begin to study sculpture seriously until he was about twenty-seven years old. He went to Italy in 1844, where he worked in Florence for some years before settling permanently in Rome. Ives made frequent trips to the United States to sell his work and found many patrons. His native state gave him commissions for the statues of Jonathan Trumbull and Roger Sherman in the United States Capitol. Though Ives was a man of intelligence and high ideals, he was limited by his lack of early training as a sculptor, and, like so many of his contemporaries, was the victim of the commonplace demands of his patrons, who asked only for pretty parlor ornaments and realistic portraits. Many of his works were turned out in quantity by the Italian marble cutters he employed. According to Ives's manuscript studio register (now in the possession of his descendants, who very kindly allowed a copy to be made of it), he sold twenty-five copies of his Rebecca at the Well, twenty-two copies of his Sans Souci, nineteen copies of his Pandora, twelve copies of his Beggar Boy, and ten copies each of his Undine and his Egeria. Almost all of these were sold to American buyers. Obviously one man alone could not turn out such a quantity of replicas. In addition to the ninety-eight "fancy pieces," he executed over one hundred and twenty portrait busts, among them portraits of Noah Webster, Professor Silliman, Park Benjamin, Thomas Sully, Henry Tuckerman, and Winfield Scott. Though the surviving members of his family remember him with lively affection, he was known among the other American sculptors and students in Rome, toward the end of his life, as "Old Bear Ives."

Rebecca at the Well   99.8

This typical Victorian piece, the original of which was made in Rome in 1854, was designed to recall the Bible story given in Genesis 24: 11–23. Between 1854 and 1894 the sculptor sold twenty-five copies, twelve of them to buyers in New York City alone. Viewed with its religious and ornamental purpose in mind, and considering the number of sales, it may be considered as one of Ives's most successful productions. Viewed as sculpture, it leads one to agree with the severely adverse opinion published by Taft in his *History of American Sculpture*.

Marble, height 50 in. Inscribed: C. B. Ives fecit Romae 1866.

REPLICAS: Twenty-five.

REFERENCES: Elwell, unpublished manuscript for a catalogue of sculpture (1903); L. Taft, *History of American Sculpture* (1930).

GIFT OF MRS. ANNA C. McCREERY, 1899.

Shobal Vail Clevenger
1812–1843

BORN in Middletown, Ohio; died at sea. Clevenger was trained in stonecutting in Cincinnati. His training gave him a technical knowledge of sculpture that was shared by few of his contemporaries, and his attractive personality won him many influential friends. His principal patron was Nicholas Longworth of Cincinnati. In his short career he modeled a number of portrait busts of prominent Americans, some of which he took to Italy to be cut in marble in 1840. Soon after his arrival in Florence he was taken ill, and he died on shipboard returning to this country with his family.

Henry Clay   36.17

This bust of Clay (1777–1852) shows the American statesman and orator at about the age of fifty-four. The original study was modeled from life in Lexington, Kentucky, about

36.17

1831, and copied in marble in Florence, Italy, by Clevenger about 1842. A writer describing this portrait in 1844 said: "It shows an already extraordinary proficiency. The dry expression, characteristic of Mr. Clay's mouth, is caught with great felicity." Though the face is treated realistically and not idealized, the shoulders of the bust are draped with a neo-classic Roman toga proper for portrait busts of statesmen. This stylistic combination, characteristic of American portrait busts of the time, is to be especially noted in the work of early nineteenth-century sculptors before they went to Italy. The careful workmanship evident in this portrait of Clay was perhaps inspired by Clevenger's admiration for his subject, as some of his other portraits in plaster seem to be rather hasty and perfunctory performances. Many old plaster copies of this bust are to be found, testifying to Clay's great popularity. This bust was deposited in the Museum as a loan in 1874 by J. Hampton Robb.

White marble, height 30¼ in.

REPLICAS: New-York Historical Society, New York (plaster); Boston Athenaeum (plaster); New York art market, 1945 (plaster).

REFERENCE: *U. S. Magazine and Democratic Review* (Feb. 1844).

GIFT OF THE ESTATE OF J. HAMPTON ROBB, 1936.

97.13.1

Thomas Crawford

c. 1813–1857

BORN presumably in New York City; died in London. After the usual apprenticeship first with a wood-carver and later with the stonecutters Frazee and Launitz, Crawford managed to sail for Italy to study sculpture in 1835. In Rome he received some instruction from Thorwaldsen. His friendship with Charles Sumner and Samuel Ward and his marriage to Ward's sister Louisa brought him invaluable social and political connections. Through these people and their friends in Washington, Crawford was awarded the largest and most important commission given to any American sculptor of the time, the commission for the sculptural decorations of the United States Capitol. His career was cut short in the midst of this work and his designs were completed by others, principally Randolph Rogers. His most important work is the Armed Freedom, a colossal figure surmounting the dome of the Capitol Building. He was the father of F. Marion Crawford, the popular novelist of the 1890's.

The Genius of Mirth   97.13.1

A letter from the sculptor, written in 1842, describes this work as "a boy of seven or eight years, dancing in great glee, and tinkling a pair of cymbals, the music of which seems to amuse him exceedingly. The sentiment is joyousness throughout. It is evident no thought of the future troubles his young mind; and he may consider himself very fortunate in being made of marble, for thus his youth remains without change." (Lester, 1846.) When this piece was presented to the Museum the donor called it Dancing Girl, and for many years it was exhibited with this erroneous title.

Marble, height 46 in. Signed: Crawford fecit. Dated: Roma MDCCCXLIII.

REFERENCES: C. E. Lester, *Artists of America* (1846); "Notable Examples of American Art in the Collection of Mrs. H[icks] L[ord]," *The Curio*, 1 (1887):97, ill.; A. Hoeber, *Treasures of the Metropolitan Museum* (1900); Elwell, unpublished manuscript for a catalogue of sculpture (1903); A. T. Gardner, *Yankee Stonecutters* (1945).

EXHIBITED: National Academy of Design, New York, 1844.

Ex coll. Henry W. Hicks, New York (1844).

GIFT OF MRS. ANNETTE W. W. HICKS-LORD, 1897.

The Dying Mexican Princess

97.13.2

A typical Victorian "fancy piece," probably based on an incident described in Prescott's *History of the Conquest of Mexico* (1843). This work has also been called The Dying Indian Girl and The Mexican Princess. Sculpturally it derives from the Greco-Roman Dead Amazon in the Naples Museum. One feature not to be overlooked is the remarkable pedestal consisting of two slabs of yellow marble separated by two urn-shaped supports of gray marble.

Marble, height 20½ in., length 52½ in. Signed: Crawford fecit. Dated: Rome 1848.

REFERENCE: "Notable Examples of American Art in the Collection of Mrs. H[icks] L[ord],"

The Curio, 1 (1887):97, ill. (as Mexican Princess).

Ex coll. Henry W. Hicks, New York.

GIFT OF MRS. ANNETTE W. W. HICKS-LORD, 1897.

The Babes in the Wood

94.9.4

This pathetic pair illustrates verses from an old English ballad, "The Norfolk Gentleman's Last Will and Testament," also known as "The Children in the Wood" or more familiarly as the nursery rhyme "The Babes in the Wood." An early version reads in part:

Thus wandered these two prettye babes,
Til deathe did end their grief
In one another's arms they dyed
As babes wanting relief:
No burial these prettye babes
Of any man receives
Til Robin-Red-Breast painfully
Did cover them with leaves.

Although contemporary writers credited Crawford with great genius and emotional sensitivity in his selection and execution of this harrowing episode, it is probable that his "inspiration" came from an engraving of the same subject that appeared in the *London Art Journal* in 1847 and from the description of the once famous monument to the Robinson children by the British sculptor Chantrey (described in Jones's biography of Chantrey published in 1849). The subject was a popular one with Victorian sentimentalists, and the

94.9.4

private collection of Queen Victoria at Osborne House contained, in the 1850's, both
a painting of the subject by John T. Peele
and a marble statue by the Belgian sculptor
Geefs. The power of Crawford's version of the
subject to arouse emotion in the beholder is
attested by a remark of Frances Eliot, who,
after the passage of forty years, wrote in 1896:
"Involuntary tears rise to my eyes as I recall
it." The children's costumes appear to be a
Victorian approximation of the style of dress
worn in France in the sixteenth century.

Marble, height 17½ in., length 48½ in. Signed:
T. C. (monogram). Dated (in cartouche)
December 31, 1851. Inscribed: The Gift of
Hamilton Fish.

REPLICA: Lenox Library, New York, 1880.

REFERENCES: H. F. Lee, *Familiar Sketches of
Sculpture and Sculptors* (1854); T. Hicks,
Eulogy on Thomas Crawford (1865); *Catalogue
of Paintings and Sculpture Exhibited to the
Public* (Lenox Library, 1880); F. Eliot, *Roman
Gossip* (1896); Elwell, unpublished manu-
script for a catalogue of sculpture (1903);
Catalogue of Sculpture (Metropolitan Muse-
um, 1908).

EXHIBITED: Metropolitan Museum, 1946.

BEQUEST OF HAMILTON FISH, 1894.

Henry Kirke Brown

1814–1886

BORN in Leyden, Massachusetts; died in
Newburgh, New York. Brown began his art
career as a boy cutting silhouettes and later
studied with the portrait painter Chester
Harding. While painting portraits in Cincinnati he took up the study of sculpture, about
1836, and for a time traveled about the country taking portraits in sculpture—many of
them in the vicinity of Albany, New York.
He went to Italy in 1842 and returned to New
York City in 1846. In his studio in Brooklyn
he made some experiments in casting his work

in bronze. His most notable work is the digni-
fied equestrian statue of Washington in Union
Square, New York. Perhaps his principal
claims to fame are his early insistence that
study in Italy was not a necessity for American sculptors and his encouragement of his
pupils—notably John Quincy Adams Ward
(see p. 30) and Edward A. Spring.

Thomas Cole   95.8.1

This bust of the American landscape painter
was probably made sometime after 1840,
when Cole was about forty. It may be said to
represent, in its bleak way, the standard, un-
inspired neoclassic portrait sculpture of the
period.

Marble, height 28¼ in.

REFERENCES: *Catalogue of Sculpture* (Metropolitan Museum, 1908); B. Cowdrey, *National
Academy of Design Exhibition Record, 1826–
1860* (1943).

EXHIBITED: National Academy of Design,
New York, 1850 (lent by Jonathan Sturges).

GIFT OF THE CHILDREN OF JONATHAN STURGES,
1895.

95.8.1

Major General Philip Kearny

00.9

Kearny (1814–1862) was one of the most brilliant and dashing military heroes of the nineteenth century, a born cavalry officer. After a brief term on the frontier at Fort Dearborn as second lieutenant in the United States Dragoons, he served under the Duke of Orleans in the Algerian Campaigns against Abdel-Kader. In the Mexican War (1846) he was aide-de-camp to General Winfield Scott. In 1859 he fought under Napoleon III at Solferino, where he won the cross of the Legion of Honor. At the beginning of the Civil War he was made Commander of the First New Jersey Brigade under General Franklin in the Army of the Potomac and was killed while reconnoitering behind the Confederate lines at Chantilly, Virginia, in 1862. His death inspired the poet Edmund C. Stedman to write his "Kearny at Seven Pines," which closes:

O, evil the black shroud of night at Chantilly
That hid him from sight of his brave men and tried!
Foul, foul sped the bullet that clipped the white lilly,
That flower of our knighthood, the whole army's pride!
Yet we dream that he still, in that shadowy region
Where the dead form their ranks at the wan drummer's sign,—
Rides on, as of old, down the length of his legion,
And the word still is Forward! along the whole line.

This portrait bust was presumably made from photographs or other portraits in 1872, possibly as a study for the statue in the United States Capitol.

Bronze, height 30 in. Signed: From H. K. Brown—Sculp. Dated 1872. Inscribed: Maj. Gen. Philip Kearny U.S.V. Killed in Battle September 1, 1862 In Memoriam A.D. 1900 by His Aide de Camp Maj. George B. Halstead U.S.V. April 16, 1861 – March 12, 1866 Jerseymen Dulce et Decorum est Pro Patria

00.9

Mon [Mori]. Founder's mark: The Henry-Bonnard Bronze Co. Founders N. Y. 1900.

REPLICA: Capitol, Washington (statue).

REFERENCE: *Catalogue of Sculpture* (Metropolitan Museum, 1908).

EXHIBITED: Duveen Brothers, New York, 1945.

GIFT OF MAJOR GEORGE B. HALSTEAD, 1900.

William Rimmer

1816–1879

BORN in Liverpool, England; died in South Milford, Massachusetts. Rimmer was brought to Nova Scotia in 1819 by his parents, who soon after settled in Boston. He received an unusual education in music, languages, and art from his father. For many years William Rimmer lived in poverty, supporting himself as a cobbler while he studied medicine. About 1855 his natural interest in art, coupled with his medical studies of anatomy, led him to experiment with sculpture. He taught a course in art anatomy at the Lowell Institute in Boston in 1861, and in 1864 he published his *Elements of Design*. He was Director of the School of Design for Women at Cooper Union in New York from 1866 to 1870, and in 1877 his *Art Anatomy* was published. Though only a half dozen pieces of his sculpture have survived and few paintings and drawings are to be found, the body of his work attests his extraordinary skill as a draftsman and sculptor and gives him a unique place in the history of American art. As a teacher his influence reached many artists who were prominent at a later day, notably John La Farge, Daniel Chester French, and William Morris Hunt.

The Museum has one drawing, a draped male figure, by Rimmer.

The Falling Gladiator   07.224

At the time this work was acquired a note in the Museum *Bulletin* stated, "Rimmer's superb conception of the statue is perfectly rep-

07.224

resented in his book on 'Art Anatomy,' known in all schools; and in this great figure of the Gladiator now placed permanently in the Museum.

"'The Falling Gladiator' was made by a young physician in the intervals of an arduous practice, in the cellar of his cottage at Milton, without artistic training, and with no other model than his own person.

"It is pleasant to note that the Museum in thus placing Dr. Rimmer's sculpture on exhibition assures for him hereafter recognition which was denied him during his lifetime."

This sculpture was made about 1860.

Bronze, height 62¾ in. Signed: W. Rimmer Sc. Caster's mark: P. P. Caproni & Bro. Plaster Casts, Boston. Founder's mark: Jno. Williams Inc. Bronze Foundry N. Y.

REPLICAS: Boston Museum of Fine Arts (bronze); Avery Library, Columbia University, New York (plaster); Smithsonian Institution, Washington, D. C. (plaster).

REFERENCES: T. H. Bartlett, *The Art Life of William Rimmer* (1882); *Met. Mus. Bull.*, old series 1 (1906):91; *Met. Mus. Bull.*, old series 2 (1907):188; *Boston Museum of Fine Arts Bull.*, 6 (1908):15; *Catalogue of Sculpture* (Metropolitan Museum, 1908); A. T. Gardner, *Yankee Stonecutters* (1945); L. Kirstein, introductory essay in *William Rimmer 1816–1879* (exhibition cat., Whitney Museum of American Art, 1946).

EXHIBITED: Boston, 1861; Paris, c. 1862; Florence, c. 1862; National Academy of Design, New York, 1866, no. 542 in cat.; Whitney Museum of American Art, New York, 1946; Newark Museum, New Jersey, 1962.

PURCHASE, ROGERS FUND, 1907.

The Dying Centaur   06.146

Though less impressive in size than The Falling Gladiator, this piece may be considered Rimmer's best existing work, one in which his technical facility and his sensitivity combined to produce a sculpture of marked quality.

The original plaster, now in the Boston Museum of Fine Arts, was made about 1871. This example was cast from the original plaster in 1906.

Bronze, height 21½ in. Signed: W. Rimmer. Founder's mark: Gorham Co. Founders.

REPLICA: Avery Library, Columbia University, New York (plaster).

REFERENCES: T. H. Bartlett, *The Art Life of William Rimmer* (1882); *Met. Mus. Bull.*, old series 1 (1906):91; *Catalogue of Sculpture* (Metropolitan Museum, 1908); A. T. Gardner, *Yankee Stonecutters* (1945); L. Kirstein, introductory essay in *William Rimmer 1816–1879* (exhibition cat., Whitney Museum of American Art, 1946).

EXHIBITED: Boston Museum of Fine Arts, 1880; Whitney Museum of American Art, New York, 1946.

GIFT OF EDWARD HOLBROOK, 1906.

Fighting Lions 07.223

The original plaster of this sculpture, made about 1871, was formerly in the Boston Art Club.

Bronze, height 16½ in. Signed: W. Rimmer. Founder's mark: Jno. Williams Inc. Bronze Foundry N. Y.

REPLICA: Avery Library, Columbia University, New York (plaster).

REFERENCES: T. H. Bartlett, *The Art Life of William Rimmer* (1882); *Met. Mus. Bull.*. old series 1 (1906):91; *Met. Mus. Bull.*, old series 2 (1907):188; *Catalogue of Sculpture* (Metropolitan Museum, 1908); A. T. Gardner, *Yankee Stonecutters* (1945); L. Kirstein, introductory essay in *William Rimmer 1816–1879* (exhibition cat., Whitney Museum of American Art, 1946).

EXHIBITED: Boston Museum of Fine Arts, 1880; Whitney Museum of American Art, New York, 1946.

GIFT OF DANIEL CHESTER FRENCH, 1907.

06.146

07.223

Erastus Dow Palmer

1817–1904

BORN in Pompey, New York; died in Albany, New York. Palmer early showed marked mechanical skill and while still quite young became an expert carpenter, builder, and pattern-maker in Utica, New York. As a pastime he took up the cutting of cameo portraits and turned to larger sculpture when the eyestrain involved in cutting cameos became too great. Palmer opened a studio in Albany, where he made portrait busts of many local men and women of prominence, as well as cemetery monuments and "ideal" figures. The strong religious cast of many of his relief medallions attracted the attention of the clergy, and his works were exhibited in New York City as the "Palmer Marbles" in the hall of the Church of the Divine Unity in 1856. One of Palmer's earliest patrons was the Honorable Hamilton Fish. For many years Palmer's studio was one of the sights of Albany, and in it were trained the young sculptors Launt Thompson (see p. 32) and Charles Calverley (see p. 33). Apparently Palmer was entirely self-taught, and he did not go to Europe until long after his reputation was made. He was awarded a medal for his statue of Robert Livingston at the Philadelphia Centennial in 1876. Though Hiram Powers was much more famous than Palmer, and though they both suffered from inexperience in their chosen art in some degree, it may be said that in general Palmer was the better sculptor. Many of the casts of his works are now in the Albany Institute of History and Art. His son Walter Launt Palmer (1854–1932) was a well-known painter who specialized in painting snowy landscapes.

94.9.2

The Indian Girl, or
The Dawn of Christianity   94.9.2

When this figure, Palmer's first full-length statue, was exhibited in New York in 1856, almost eight pages of prose and poem were devoted to the description of it in the catalogue of the exhibition. Briefly, the story is as follows: An Indian girl, wandering in the forest collecting bright-colored feathers, suddenly finds a crucifix dropped by one of the early French Catholic missionary fathers, and "the maiden, hitherto taught by simple nature, stands on the threshold of womanhood, and Christianity, the divine answer to the best longings of the soul . . . awaits her." The plaster original of this figure is in the Albany Institute of History and Art. A painting of the interior of Palmer's studio by T. H. Matteson, also in the Albany Institute, shows The Indian Girl in the background.

Marble, height 59½ in. Signed: E. D. Palmer, Sc. Dated 1856. Inscribed: The Gift of Hamilton Fish.

REFERENCES: *Catalogue of the Palmer Marbles* (exhibition cat., Hall of the Church of the Divine Unity, 1856); *Catalogue of Sculpture* (Metropolitan Museum, 1908).

EXHIBITED: Hall of the Church of the Divine Unity, New York, 1856.

BEQUEST OF HAMILTON FISH, 1894.

The White Captive 94.9.3

The subject of this work was probably drawn from one of the popular accounts of the adventures and sufferings of women who had been carried off from frontier settlements to captivity among the Indians. From 1859 until 1894 this figure was one of the principal ornaments of Hamilton Fish's house in Stuyvesant Square, New York. In his *History of American Sculpture* Taft praised it as the best piece of American sculpture up to that time. He called it "one of the most charming things yet done by an American sculptor, and one of the earliest to show the quality of expressiveness. . . . The movement of the torso is grace itself. . . . To think that anything so refined and sympathetic should have been carved in this country in 1858! It is not strange that we should have poets who could imagine radiant beauty; but that an unschooled hand should model with such a combination of tenderness and firmness, that it should create at the same time elegance of pose and eloquence of appeal in a work of rare perfection is indeed a marvel. In all those years nothing so fine had come over the seas from Italy; nothing so original, so dramatic, so human; nothing that could approach it even in charm of workmanship." The original plaster figure is in the Albany Institute of History and Art.

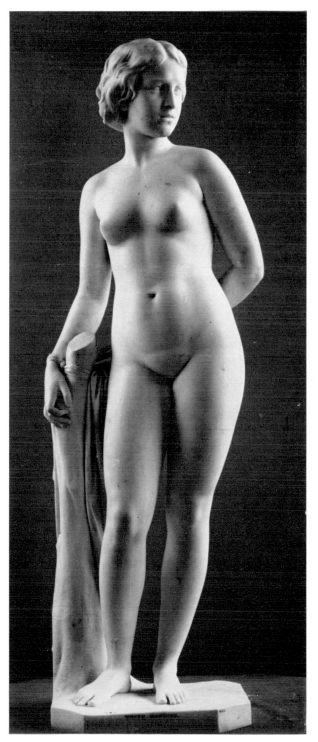

94.9.3

Marble, height 66 in. Signed: E. D. Palmer, Sc. Dated 1859. Inscribed: The Gift of Hamilton Fish.

REFERENCES: A. Chester, "Erastus Dow Palmer," *Cosmopolitan Art Journal*, 2 (1858); J. J. Jarves, *The Art Idea* (1864); *Catalogue of Sculpture* (Metropolitan Museum, 1908); L. Taft, *History of American Sculpture* (1930), pp. 136 f.; A. T. Gardner, *Yankee Stonecutters* (1945).

BEQUEST OF HAMILTON FISH, 1894.

Edward Augustus Brackett

1818–1908

BORN in Vassalboro, Maine; died in Winchester, Massachusetts. Brackett was taken in 1835 to Cincinnati and there began his art studies independently about 1839. He is reported to have made portrait busts in Cincinnati, Washington, and New York. While living in New York, he met the poet Bryant and the sculptress Cornelia DuBois and was befriended by Anne Charlotte Lynch. In 1841 he went to Boston with letters of introduction to Dana, Longfellow, and Allston. In 1848 he began his great work, The Shipwrecked Mother and Child, which he completed in marble in 1851 and sold to the Boston Athenaeum. Brackett designed and built his own house in Winchester, near Boston, and there he experimented in raising game birds and hothouse grapes. His growing interest in things of this sort led him gradually to give up sculpture, especially after he became connected with the Massachusetts Fish and Game Commission. His interests also embraced the writing of poetry, of which three volumes were published.

In 1903 his wife wrote a letter to the Museum telling of his later years, in which she says: "He gave up his studio in 1873—has done nothing in that line since having been at the head of the Mass. Fish and Game Com-

mission for nearly a third of a century—is still an active member although relieved of the more arduous duties—is now 84 years of age, keen of intellect—has written and published a little book of essays since his last birthday in the line of 'The New Thought' and psychic subjects, 'The World We Live In'. The 'Shipwrecked Mother and Child' . . . has again been placed in his hands and will be heard from erelong. We still have 'Little Nell', a marble bust of *Alston* [sic] and of Genl. Butler and several plaster casts of notable men." Brackett was the brother of the once well-known Boston fish painter Walter M. Brackett.

Washington Allston   95.8.2

Allston (1779–1843), American painter and poet, speaking in praise of Brackett's work, said: "His busts show, that in the rare power of expressing character and intellect, he has few equals" (Lee). This bust was made about 1844 from a death mask taken by Brackett. When the portrait was completed the sculptor was moved to compose the following poem:

Lines Suggested on Finishing a Bust of Washington Allston

Upwards unto the living light,
Intensely thou dost gaze,
As if thy very soul would seek,
In that far distant maze,
Communion with those heavenly forms,
That, lifting to the sight
Their golden wings and snowy robes
Float in a sea of light, . . .
How strangely have the swift hours flown,
As o'er the shapeless pile
I poured the strength of my full soul,
Lost to all else the while.
When fell the last faint stroke which told
That thou and I must part,
That all of life that I could give
Was thine, how throbbed my heart! . . .
Thou who wast kind and good and great,
Thy task on earth is done
Of those that walked in beauty's light
Thou wast the chosen one.

95.8.2

Marble, height 26 in. Signed: Brackct. Sc.

REPLICAS: New-York Historical Society, New York; Pennsylvania Academy of the Fine Arts, Philadelphia; collection of the sculptor, Boston, 1903.

REFERENCES: E. A. Brackett, *Twilight Hours; or Leisure Moments of an Artist* (1845); H. F. Lee, *Familiar Sketches of Sculpture and Sculptors* (1854); *Catalogue of Sculpture* (Metropolitan Museum, 1908); A. T. Gardner, "Memorials of an American Romantic," *Met. Mus. Bull.*, new series 3 (1944):54.

EXHIBITED: National Academy of Design, New York, 1850 (lent by Jonathan Sturges).

GIFT OF THE CHILDREN OF JONATHAN STURGES, 1895.

William Wetmore Story
1819–1895

BORN in Salem, Massachusetts; died in Vallombrosa, Italy. Story was the son of Joseph Story, a Justice of the United States Supreme Court. He was educated at Harvard University, and after his graduation from the Harvard Law School in 1840 he decided to become a sculptor. In 1856 he settled permanently in Rome and was an important member of the colony of American artists living there. His literary works—poems, essays, biographies—and his political and social connections, including the marriage of his daughter with an Italian princeling of the Medici family, as well as the popularity of his sculptural works, cast about him a glamour enjoyed by no other American artist of his time. A few years after his death his biography, *William Wetmore Story and His Friends*, was written by Henry James. Story's sons both became artists, Julian a painter, Waldo a sculptor.

Cleopatra   88.5

This statue was one of the most famous and popular works by any American sculptor of the mid-nineteenth century. Hawthorne's description of it in his book *The Marble Faun* (1861) gave it a wide popularity among English and American novel-readers, and when it was exhibited in the Roman section of the London Exposition of 1862 it established an international reputation for the sculptor. For many years the brilliant social position of the artist and the literary connotations of the subject obscured the fact that Story's Cleopatra was a rather tiresome essay in stonecutting. At least three versions of the subject were made, and it is believed that there were several replicas of each version. The first version was made in 1858, the second in 1864, the third in 1884 and 1885. In 1892 Story was asking eight thousand dollars apiece for copies.

88.5

The sculptor also composed a long poem entitled "Cleopatra" published in his volume of poems *Graffiti d'Italia* (1868).

Marble, height 54½ in. Signed: W W S (monogram). Dated: Roma 1869. Inscribed: Cleopatra.

REPLICAS: Goldsmiths' Company Hall, London, 1897; collection of Mrs. Paran Stevens, New York, 1897; collection of Count Palffy, Paris, 1897.

REFERENCES: N. Hawthorne, *The Marble Faun* (1861), and *Italian Notebooks* (1871); M. Phillips, *Reminiscences of William Wetmore Story* (1897); H. James, *William Wetmore Story and His Friends* (1903); A. T. Gardner, *Met. Mus. Bull.*, new series 2 (1943):147.

GIFT OF JOHN TAYLOR JOHNSTON, 1888.

Medea   94.8

Medea, seeking revenge on her faithless husband, murdered their two children. The contemporary attitude toward this work, which was designed in 1864, is revealed in the remark

of a visitor to Story's studio: "This is Medea with her stormy heart chained and still in marble; no actress's ravings ever told the story so well." Story also wrote a poem *Medea Meditating the Death of Her Children*.

Marble, height 76½ in. Signed: W S (monogram). Dated: Roma 1868.

REPLICAS: Three marble replicas were made.

REFERENCES: W. J. Clark, *Great American Sculptures* (1877); M. Phillips, *Reminiscences of William Wetmore Story* (1897); *Catalogue of Sculpture* (Metropolitan Museum, 1908).

EXHIBITED: Centennial Exposition, Philadelphia, 1876.

GIFT OF HENRY CHAUNCEY, 1894.

Salome   97.9

Henry James describes this figure as "the panting, resting daughter of Herodias." It is perhaps the most vacuous of all Story's works.

Marble, height 57 in. Signed: W S (monogram). Dated: Roma 1871.

REFERENCES: M. Phillips, *Reminiscences of William Wetmore Story* (1897); H. James, *William Wetmore Story and His Friends* (1903); *Catalogue of Sculpture* (Metropolitan Museum, 1908).

GIFT OF WILLIAM NELSON, 1896.

Thomas Ball

1819–1911

BORN in Charlestown, Massachusetts; died in Montclair, New Jersey. Ball inherited his interest in art from his father, an only moderately successful sign painter. His father's death made it necessary for him to leave school in order to help support his mother and sisters. For a time he worked in the New England Museum in Boston where he was employed to clean the glass cases and repair the waxworks figures. While he was in the museum he became interested in the portraits displayed there and began to copy them. Soon he set himself up as a portrait painter and miniaturist. At the suggestion of a friend he also tried his hand at modeling in clay. Much of the time while he was thus employed he was obliged to add to his income by singing. In 1848 he sang the title role of Elijah at the first performance of that oratorio in this country. In 1854, deciding to make sculpture his life work, he went to Florence, where he remained until 1897 except for several years spent in Boston making an equestrian Washington for the Public Gardens. Old age forced him to retire to the home of his daughter in Montclair, New Jersey. In 1876 and 1877 Daniel Chester French was his pupil. Thomas Ball's autobiography *My Three Score Years and Ten* gives an interesting account of the sunnier side of his career, and reveals the author as a man blessed with a great deal of charm and simplicity of character.

Daniel Webster 13.214

In his autobiography Ball relates his desire as a boy to paint Daniel Webster's "godlike head." "Strange as it may seem," he writes, "after my short experience, I now felt confident that I could model a head of Webster." He describes the failure of his first attempt, a small bust, and his resolve to undertake immediately his first life-size bust, one of Daniel Webster. It was completed, according to Ball, only a day or two before Webster's death. "At such a time [it] attracted a good deal of attention. It was pronounced a wonderful success, and numerous demands were made for casts of it." Ball repeated it for the full-length statue of his Webster Monument in Central Park, New York. The bust was given to the Museum by Ball's daughter, the wife of the sculptor William Couper.

White marble, height 30 in. (heroic scale). Signed: T. Ball. Dated 1868.

REFERENCE: Thomas Ball, *My Three Score Years and Ten* (1892), pp. 136 ff.

GIFT OF MRS. WILLIAM COUPER, 1913.

13.214

William Morris Hunt

1824–1879

BORN in Brattleboro, Vermont; died at Appledore, one of the Isles of Shoals. As a young man Hunt aspired, after cutting a few cameo portraits, to become a sculptor. In 1843 he traveled to Rome with his mother, and there he studied briefly with Henry Kirke Brown. The Roman climate proving inimical to his delicate health, he proceeded to Düsseldorf to continue his studies. Here he rebelled against the teaching methods and set out for Paris to study with the sculptor Pradier. While wandering through Paris he saw a portrait painted by Couture, which decided him to become a painter and a pupil of that artist. After he returned to Boston, Hunt became one of the most influential teachers of his time, and he was largely instrumental in turning young American artists from study in Rome or Munich to the ateliers of Paris and Barbizon. Thus Hunt is usually known as a painter and teacher, and his works in sculpture are very rare. He introduced the paintings of the Barbizon school and the bronze animal sculptures of Barye to American collectors, making them coveted treasures for museums and collectors to bid for. Hunt was noted for his sharp tongue and acid wit as well as for his delightfully shocking Bohemian eccentricities. He was drowned while staying with the Thaxters at Appledore, Isles of Shoals, possibly a suicide.

The Horses of Anahita, or The Flight of Night   80.12

In 1846 Hunt received from his brother Leavitt a translation of a Persian poem about Anahita, the goddess of night, which fired his imagination. He immediately set about translating the poem into a picture. Having some difficulty in drawing the "fearful plunge" of the "well-trained coursers" attached to the chariot of the goddess, Hunt modeled the three horses in relief. But the composition fascinated him, and he painted it many times. Once the design was painted on a tea tray, which was then framed in gold plush and hung in his sister's parlor. When Hunt's studio was burned in the great fire in Boston (1872), all his sketches and studies for Anahita were destroyed. The tea tray, a small photograph, and the original clay model of the horses were all that remained of his labor. In 1878, when he was awarded a commission to paint two large murals for the new State Capitol at Albany, New York, it was almost inevitable that the long considered and much amended design for Anahita would be chosen for one of them. The title was changed, for the benefit of the American public, to The Flight of Night. The exertion and strain of painting these murals under difficult conditions and in the time required resulted in Hunt's nervous collapse. He died in 1879, shortly after they were completed. The following year, his brother, the architect Richard Morris Hunt, presented this cast of the horses to the Museum.

Plaster relief painted brown, height 18½ in., width 28½ in. (framed in walnut molding).

REPLICAS: Private collection (formerly in collection of R. M. Hunt, Newport, Rhode Island, 1880); private collection (formerly in collection of James Gregerson, Boston, 1880); Isabella Stewart Gardner Museum, Boston. Plaster replicas were being sold in Boston as late as 1929 by a plaster firm there.

REFERENCES: *William Morris Hunt Memorial Exhibition* (Boston Museum of Fine Arts, 1879–1880); T. H. Bartlett, "The Art Life of William Morris Hunt," *Metropolitan Museum Handbook*, no. 6 (Apr.-Oct. 1880); H. C. Angell, *Records of William Morris Hunt* (1881); H. M. Knowlton, *The Art Life of William Morris Hunt* (1899); A. T. Gardner, "A Rebel in Patagonia," *Met. Mus. Bull.*, new series 3 (1945):224.

EXHIBITED: Boston Museum of Fine Arts, 1879–1880.

GIFT OF RICHARD MORRIS HUNT, 1880.

Wilson MacDonald

1824–1908

James Wilson Alexander MacDonald. Born in Steubenville, Ohio; died in Yonkers, New York. MacDonald showed artistic talents at an early age and, at sixteen, on seeing a bust of Washington, decided to become a sculptor. His father wanted to apprentice him in the blacksmith's trade, but MacDonald had no enthusiasm for it and ran away from home, finally making his way to St. Louis, where he found employment in a publishing house. He studied art during his free time in the studio of a local painter. After several years he became a senior partner in the publishing firm. In 1849 he went to New York to continue his art studies, and shortly thereafter he retired from business to settle in New York and devote all his time to sculpture and painting. MacDonald executed many portrait busts and a number of Civil War monuments. Some of his time was spent in writing and lecturing on

art. At one time he owned what was reputed to be the original plaster bust of George Washington by Houdon, and he made and sold many copies of it. Many of his portraits were made from life masks and death masks. In general his works are monotonously realistic and lifeless. Lorado Taft, however, writing in 1903, gave a favorable opinion of him: "MacDonald has long been a picturesque figure in the world of monumental art, and has done much creditable work."

Brigadier General Winfield Scott Hancock   86.4

Bust of Winfield Scott Hancock (1824–1886), soldier and politician. General Hancock graduated from West Point in 1844 in the same class with Generals Grant, McClellan, Franklin, Smith, Reynolds, Rosecrans, Lyon, Longstreet, and Stonewall Jackson. He was cited in Congress for his part in the battle of Gettysburg. In 1880 he was nominated Democratic candidate for president but was defeated by Garfield. In his memoirs General Grant says of Hancock, "Tall, well-formed, . . . young and fresh-looking, he presented an appearance that would attract the attention of an army as he passed."

This bust, marked with an undecipherable date but probably made about 1880, was possibly made from a life mask. In 1891 a large replica was presented to the City of New York and erected in Hancock Square at Manhattan Avenue and 123 Street. The bust was given to the Museum by Benjamin Field, one of its Founders.

Bronze, height 27½ in. Signed: Wilson MacDonald.

REFERENCES: Almira R. Hancock, *Reminiscences of Winfield Scott Hancock* (1887); *Catalogue of Sculpture* (Metropolitan Museum, 1908); *Catalogue of Works of Art Belonging to New York City* (1909).

EX COLL. General Winfield Scott Hancock, New York.

GIFT OF BENJAMIN HAZARD FIELD, 1886.

William Henry Rinehart

1825–1874

BORN in Union Bridge, Maryland; died in Rome. As a youth Rinehart showed no interest in schooling or in farming; he was apprenticed to a local stonecutter. Later he went to Baltimore, where he worked in Sisson's marble yard and attended art classes in the Maryland Institute of Mechanic Arts. His work as a marble cutter attracted some attention and in 1855 he was enabled to go to Rome. In 1858, after a visit to Baltimore, he settled permanently in Rome. His principal patron was the art collector William T. Walters of Baltimore, father of Henry Walters. At Rinehart's death in 1874 it was found that he had left his modest estate in trust, "Being desirous of aiding in the promotion of a more highly cultivated taste for art among the people of my native state and of assisting young men in the Study of the Art of Sculpture, who may desire to make it a Profession." Through the care of his executors, William Walters and B. F. Newcomer, the Rinehart Fund was greatly increased and from time to time scholarships have been awarded to young sculptors for study in Italy or France. The first sculptor

to have the advantage of a Rinehart Scholarship was the animal sculptor A. Phimister Proctor, who in 1895 was awarded a five-year scholarship to study in Paris. In 1896 a similar scholarship was awarded to Hermon A. MacNeil for study in Rome. These scholarships and the Rinehart School of Sculpture at the Maryland Institute form a notable memorial to him.

Antigone   91.4

The full title of this piece is Antigone Pouring a Libation over the Corpse of Her Brother Polynices. It represents a crucial moment from the Greek tragedy *Antigone* by Sophocles. This figure was commissioned by John H. Hall in 1867 and completed in 1870. Hall gave the sculptor freedom to choose any subject. In a letter of 1867 the artist stated, "I am now modeling a life sized statue of Antigone from Sophocles." The original plaster is in the Peabody Institute in Baltimore. In 1881 the work was lent to this Museum by Hall, and on his death in 1891 it was presented to the Museum as a memorial to him.

Marble, height 71½ in. Signed: Wm. H. Rinehart, Sculpt. Dated 1870.

REPLICA: Peabody Institute, Baltimore (marble reduction).

REFERENCES: W. H. Rinehart, manuscript letters to Frank B. Mayer (1853–1870); W. S. Rusk, *William Henry Rinehart* (1939); C. M. Ross and A. W. Rutledge, *A Catalogue of the Work of William Henry Rinehart* (1948).

GIFT OF THE FAMILY OF JOHN H. HALL, 1891.

Clytie   11.68.1

Clytie was a water nymph who for her constant love of the sun god, Apollo, was changed into a sunflower.

Marble, height 62⅜ in. Signed: Wm. H. Rinehart. Sculp. Dated: Roma 1872.

REPLICAS: Peabody Institute, Baltimore (marble); private collection, Scotland (marble). A

05.12

large marble replica was formerly in a private collection in Cleveland, Ohio; a small marble replica was formerly in a private collection in England. Three plaster casts are known to have been made but can no longer be found.

REFERENCES: W. H. Rinehart, manuscript letters to Frank B. Mayer (1853–1870); W. S. Rusk, *William Henry Rinehart* (1939); C. M. Ross and A. W. Rutledge, *A Catalogue of the Work of William Henry Rinehart* (1948).

EXHIBITED: Newark Museum, New Jersey 1962.

GIFT OF MR. AND MRS. WILLIAM H. HERRIMAN, 1911.

Latona and Her Children
Apollo and Diana   05.12

This sculpture of Latona, goddess of night, with her children by Jupiter, was commissioned in 1871. It was completed after Rinehart's death, and deposited in the Museum in 1875. The original plaster is in the Peabody Institute in Baltimore.

Marble, height 46 in. Signed: Wm. H. Rinehart. Sculpt. Dated: Romae 1874.

REFERENCES: W. H. Rinehart, manuscript letters to Frank B. Mayer (1853–1870); W. S. Rusk, *William Henry Rinehart* (1939); C. M. Ross and A. W. Rutledge, *A Catalogue of the Work of William Henry Rinehart* (1948).

EX COLL. Edward C. T. Lewis, Hoboken, New Jersey.

PURCHASE, ROGERS FUND, 1905.

Randolph Rogers

1825–1892

BORN in Waterloo, New York; died in Rome. As a child Rogers was taken by his parents to live in Ann Arbor, Michigan. In his youth he worked at various jobs, and he had some success in selling his cartoons and drawings. As a young man he came to New York to work for

a firm of drygoods merchants, who were so favorably impressed with his artistic abilities that they lent him funds to go to Florence to study sculpture with Bartolini in 1848. In 1855 he settled permanently in Rome. On the death of Thomas Crawford in 1857 Rogers was given the task of completing some of the work Crawford had been commissioned to do for the Capitol in Washington. Rogers made frequent trips to the United States and was very successful in winning commissions for monuments. He was for many years one of the leading figures of the American colony in Rome. His "fancy pieces" Ruth and Nydia were among the most popular sculptures shown at the Philadelphia Centennial in 1876, and many copies of them were sold. Rogers was elected a Councilor of the Academy of Saint Luke in Rome.

He retired in 1882 and in 1886 presented many of the plaster originals from his studio in Rome to the University of Michigan Museum of Art, and at his death more casts from his studio were added to the gift, bringing the total of his works at Ann Arbor to about two hundred.

Ruth Gleaning   99.7.1

This work illustrates the story given in the Book of Ruth II:1–13. It is reputed to be the first "ideal" subject designed by Rogers after his arrival in Italy. This example was purchased at the sculptor's studio in Rome in 1855 by the father of the donor, James H. Douglas, who lent it for exhibition at the Philadelphia Centennial Exposition in 1876. Its pose in general is adapted from a Greco-Roman statue of one of the daughters of Niobe. The original plaster is in the University of Michigan Museum of Art in Ann Arbor.

Marble, height 45¾ in.

REPLICAS: Probably as many as twenty replicas were made. Two examples appeared on the New York art market in 1948.

REFERENCES: W. J. Clark, *Great American Sculptures* (1877); M. D'Ooge, *Catalogue of*

99.7.1

the Gallery of Art and Archaeology at the University of Michigan (1892); L. Taft, *History of American Sculpture* (1930).

EXHIBITED: Centennial Exposition, Philadelphia, 1876.

GIFT OF JAMES H. DOUGLAS, 1899.

Nydia   99.7.2

Nydia is a character in the novel *The Last Days of Pompeii* (1834) by Bulwer-Lytton. This was perhaps the most popular piece of sculpture made by any American during the nineteenth century. A hundred copies in marble are believed to have been sold during the sculptor's lifetime. The pose and drapery of the figure are an adaptation of the famous Greco-Roman sculpture called The Old Market Woman, in the Vatican Gallery. The

original plaster is in the University of Michigan Museum of Art. This particular copy was one of the first ones made. It was purchased in Rome in 1859, the first year Rogers put this subject on sale. It also has the distinction of being the one that was exhibited in Philadelphia at the Centennial Exposition in 1876. A visitor to Rogers' studio remarked, "I went to his studio and saw seven Nydias, all in a row, all listening, all groping, and seven marble-cutters at work, cutting them out. It was a gruesome sight."

The old gallery catalogues, in describing this piece, usually quote the following passage from the novel to refresh the memory of the gallery visitor. This quotation sums up so much that Victorian art-lovers sought for in "modern" sculpture that it is worth quoting at length. It discovers our heroine in the midst of the volcanic eruption and earthquake that destroyed Pompeii:

"Meanwhile Nydia, when separated by the throng from Glaucus and Ione, had in vain endeavored to regain them. In vain she raises the plaintive cry so peculiar to the blind; it was lost amid a thousand shrieks of more selfish terror. . . . Guiding her steps, then, by the staff which she always carried, she continued with incredible dexterity to avoid the masses of ruin that encumbered the path—to thread the streets; and unerringly (so blessed now was that accustomed darkness so afflicting in ordinary life!) to take the nearest direction to the seaside.

"Poor girl! her courage was beautiful to behold! and Fate seemed to favor one so helpless. The boiling torrents touched her not, save by the general rain which accompanied them, the huge fragments of scoria shivered the pavement before and beside her, but spared that frail form. . . .

"Weak, exposed, yet fearless, supported but by one wish, she was the very emblem of Psyche in her wanderings;—of Hope, walking through the Valley of the Shadow; a very emblem of the Soul itself—lone but comforted, amid the dangers and the snares of life!" (Bulwer-Lytton, *The Last Days of Pompeii*, edition of 1835, vol. 2, p. 189.)

Marble, height 55 in. Signed: Randolph
Rogers. Dated: Rome 1859.

REPLICAS: University of Michigan Museum
of Art, Ann Arbor (marble); Pennsylvania
Academy of the Fine Arts, Philadelphia (marble); Princeton University, Princeton, New
Jersey (marble); New York Public Library
(marble); Newark Museum, New Jersey. According to Lorado Taft one hundred replicas
in marble were made and sold during the
sculptor's lifetime.

REFERENCES: E. Bulwer-Lytton, *The Last
Days of Pompeii* (1834); *International Exhibition 1876, Official Catalogue*, part II (Philadelphia, 1876); W. J. Clark, *Great American
Sculptures* (1877); M. D'Ooge, *Catalogue of
the Gallery of Art and Archaeology at the University of Michigan* (1892); A. Hoeber, *Art
Treasures of the Metropolitan Museum of Art*
(1899); *Catalogue of Sculpture* (Metropolitan
Museum, 1908); D. M. Armstrong, *Day Before Yesterday* (1920); L. Taft, *History of
American Sculpture* (1930).

99.7.2

EXHIBITED: Centennial Exposition, Philadelphia, 1876; Southern Exposition, Louisville,
Kentucky, 1883 (offered for sale at $1250).

GIFT OF JAMES H. DOUGLAS, 1899.

Indian Group — The Last Shot

05.13.1

This sculpture of an Indian on a rearing horse,
just having shot his last arrow, with a wounded
Indian on the ground beneath him, is reputed
to be Rogers' last work, made just before his
retirement in 1882.

Bronze, height 45 in. Signed: Randolph
Rogers, Rome. Dated 1880.

REPLICA: University of Michigan Museum
of Art, Ann Arbor.

REFERENCES: M. D'Ooge, *Catalogue of the
Gallery of Art and Archaeology at the Univer-
sity of Michigan* (1892); *Catalogue of Sculpture*
(Metropolitan Museum, 1908).

BEQUEST OF HENRY H. COOK, 1905.

Leonard Wells Volk

1828–1895

BORN in Wellstown, New York; died in Chicago. At the age of sixteen Volk began to learn
stonecutting in his father's shop. For a time
he was an itinerant workman in various parts
of Massachusetts and New York. In 1848 he
settled in St. Louis, where he began to study
art with a view to becoming a sculptor, while
supporting himself as a stonecutter. One of
Volk's first works in marble was a copy of
Joel Hart's bust of Henry Clay. In 1855, with
money lent him by his relative Stephen A.
Douglas, Volk went to Rome, where he remained for almost two years. On his return to
the United States in 1857 he settled permanently in Chicago and became a leader in art
activities. He was one of the founders of the
Chicago Academy of Design in 1867 and its
president for a number of years.

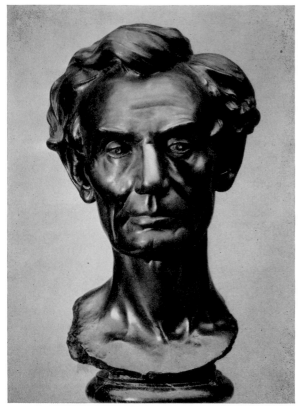

14.92

trait bust and the original plaster life mask in the Smithsonian Institution, Washington, reveals the many changes the sculptor made, idealizing his finished work. This cast was made about 1914 for Theodore B. Starr, Inc., from an old plaster copy.

Bronze, height 20¾ in. Inscribed: Abraham Lincoln Modelled from Life by Leonard W. Volk Chicago 1860 Replica. Founder's mark: S. Klaber & Co. Founders N. Y.

REPLICA: Art Institute of Chicago (bronze).

REFERENCES: *Biographical Sketches of the Leading Men of Chicago* (1868); L. W. Volk, "The Lincoln Life Mask and How It Was Made," *The Century Magazine*, 1 (1881):213; "Portraits of Lincoln," *McClure's Magazine*, 10 (1898):339; T. H. Bartlett, "Physiognomy of Lincoln," *McClure's Magazine*, 29 (1907):391; R. W. Gilder, "On the Life Mask of Lincoln" (poem), *Home Progress*, 3 (1914):300.

EXHIBITED: Paris, 1867.

GIFT OF THEODORE B. STARR, INC., 1914.

His fame as a sculptor rests principally, if not solely, on his portrait bust of Abraham Lincoln, modeled after a life mask cast in Chicago in 1860. Volk's design for the bust of Lincoln was patented in 1860, and after Lincoln's death Volk sold many plaster copies of it. The original life mask in plaster is now in the United States National Museum, Smithsonian Institution. This mask and the bust by Volk have been used by all later sculptors in making portraits of Lincoln.

Volk's son was the painter Douglas Volk (1856–1935).

Abraham Lincoln   14.92

This head was made in 1860 when Lincoln was fifty-one years old and a candidate for president. A comparison between this por-

John Rogers
1829–1904

BORN in Salem, Massachusetts; died in New Canaan, Connecticut. In 1902 Rogers dictated the following autobiographical sketch in answer to the Museum's request for information. It has not been published before.

"After leaving school, at sixteen years of age, he tried various employments but did not find anything congenial as he was always anxious to follow his artistic bent, to which his relatives had objected, thinking it a poor reliance as a support.

"About 1850 he took a trip to Europe and spent three months in Rome, in the studio of Mr. Spence, an English sculptor, in order to try whether he [Mr. Spence] could make his knowledge of modelling available. This comprised all the instruction he ever received. He found however all the criticisms he could get were based on the classic style, which did not interest him particularly.

"On his return from Europe he engaged again in business for a few years. Afterwards he came to New York, Dec. 1860, bringing in his trunk the model of the 'Slave Auction,' also a letter introducing him to an Italian who understood casting intricate figures in elastic moulds. He made an arrangement with this man to make duplicates of 'The Slave Auction' model, while Mr. Rogers stood by to watch the process. He then collected the materials and fitted up in his room the appliances necessary for the work and after hard work and many failures succeeded in fair results, and he soon became a master of this trade. From this time he employed his own workmen, and after making the 'Slave Auction,' he designed the 'Checker Players.' Soon after this the war broke out and he made 'The Picket Guard' which was very popular. . . . and in 1863 the 'One More Shot.'

"The process of casting in elastic moulds required them to be renewed about once every day. This was done by melting the mould and pouring it over the model, where it was left till chilled before it could be opened and handled. This was found to be a very wearing process on the originals, and Mr. Rogers found it necessary to make these originals in bronze, very carefully worked up, so that all the groups made after the 'Union Refugees' are from these bronze originals. . . . At the conclusion of the war Mr. Rogers selected more social subjects like 'The Charity Patient.' . . . He also made several groups from Shakespeare. . . . Besides these he made two groups of larger size. . . . He also made an equestrian statue of Gen'l John F. Reynolds which stands at the entrance to the City Hall in Philadelphia. A statue of President Lincoln followed, which received a bronze medal, the highest award from the Columbian Exposition. It now belongs to the city of Manchester, New Hampshire.

"The groups varied in their popularity; which was demonstrated by their sales: 'Coming to the Parson' proved the most popular, 8000 copies being called for. 'Checkers up at the Farm' came next, the demand being for 5000 copies, . . . altogether the sales numbered about eighty-thousand (80,000). Mr. Rogers has received a large number of medals and diplomas from various exhibitions of his works.

"Mr. Rogers artistic work covers the period from 1860 to 1895, when he was obliged to give it up, owing to ill-health. In 1865 he married Harriet Moore Francis of New York City." Rogers was elected a National Academician in 1863.

The ill health that caused Rogers to give up his work was *paralysis agitans* of such severity that he was confined to his room. Mrs. Rogers, who actually wrote the above sketch, said in an accompanying letter: "I would like to add that my husband is now too much of an invalid to write at all, so I have written the enclosed at his dictation (a great effort for him!)." Rogers died at his home in New Canaan, Connecticut, of pneumonia, July 26, 1904.

"Wounded to the Rear"— One More Shot 17.174

In the catalogue of Rogers' work issued in 1877 this subject is described as follows: "Two wounded soldiers have been ordered to the rear during battle, but one of them is taking out a cartridge to load up again, determined to have one more shot before leaving." In the 1870's plaster copies of this piece were sold for fifteen dollars each. This subject was also reproduced in slightly smaller scale in Parian ware.

Bronze, height 23½ in. Signed (on the soldier's knapsack): John Rogers 14 W. 12 St. New York. Dated 1865. Inscribed (on base): "Wounded to the Rear" One More Shot. Patented Jan. 17. 1865.

REPLICAS: New-York Historical Society, New York (plaster). Hundreds of plaster copies are believed to have been made and sold during the sculptor's lifetime.

REFERENCES: J. Rogers, *Groups of Statuary by John Rogers* (illustrated advertising catalogue,

17.174

1877); *Catalogue of Sculpture* (Metropolitan Museum, 1908); C. Smith, *Rogers Groups* (1934).

EXHIBITED: Centennial Exposition, Philadelphia, 1876.

EX COLL. Alexander P. Rogers, New York.

PURCHASE, ROGERS FUND, 1917.

George Washington   44.75

This statuette of George Washington (1732–1799) was made in 1875. The face is based on Houdon's portrait of Washington.

Bronze, height 29¼ in. Signed: John Rogers, New York. Inscribed: Washington.

REPLICAS: New-York Historical Society, New York (plaster). Hundreds of plaster copies are thought to have been made and sold during the sculptor's lifetime. A Boston plaster firm was still offering copies of this in 1928 for eighteen dollars.

REFERENCE: C. Smith, *Rogers Groups* (1934).

EXHIBITED: Centennial Exposition, Philadelphia, 1876.

GIFT OF WILLIAM LEANDER POST, 1944.

John Quincy Adams Ward
1830–1910

BORN in Urbana, Ohio; died in New York. At the age of nineteen Ward gained admission to the studio of the sculptor Henry Kirke Brown (see p. 12), where he remained as student and studio assistant for seven years. During this period he did much work on his master's equestrian statue of George Washington, now in Union Square, New York. In 1861 Ward was employed by the Ames Company as a designer of small decorative objects such as sword hilts, cane handles, and inkwells, cast in silver, gold, and bronze. One of his first large works, The Indian Hunter, completed in 1864, was purchased by a group of prominent citizens and presented to the Central Park Commissioners for installation in the park. From this time forward Ward was seldom without commissions for portraits or monuments. His Seventh Regiment Memorial, a dejected Union soldier leaning on a rifle, also in Central Park, was the model for many other Civil War monuments. His Puritan and his Shakespeare, both also in Central Park, typify the rather paltry post-Civil-War "galvanized" statues.

Ward was elected a member of the National Academy of Design in 1863 and a member of the Board of Trustees of this Museum at its founding in 1870. He was one of four professional artists on the Board of Trustees and served as a member of the Executive Committee until 1901. In 1874 he was elected President of the National Academy of Design. When the National Sculpture Society was organized in 1893 he became by unanimous vote its first president and served in that capacity until 1905. In 1882 he built a house and studio, designed by his friend Richard Morris Hunt, on West 52nd Street. Most of his larger monuments were made there, and its elaborate reception room, frescoed and furnished in the Pompeian manner, became a landmark in conservative upper Bohemian circles. Ward was a member of the American Academy of Arts and Letters, the American Institute of Architects, the National Arts Club, and the Century Association. His connection with all these organizations, his impressive social contacts, his ability as a raconteur, and his prowess as a woodsman and fisherman gave him a prestige and power matched by no other American artist of his generation. In 1902, at the age of seventy-two, he was commissioned to execute the sculptural decoration for the pediment of the New York Stock Exchange. In designing this large project he was assisted by Paul Bartlett, who modeled the figures, and by Getulio Piccirilli, who enlarged the models to the proper scale and executed all the actual stone-cutting.

William Tilden Blodgett 10.200

Bust of William Tilden Blodgett (1823–1875), American philanthropist, Founder, Trustee, Vice-President and Chairman of the Executive Committee of the Board of Trustees of the Metropolitan Museum.

Marble, height 26 in.

REFERENCES: R. W. de Forest, "William Tilden Blodgett and the Beginnings of the Metropolitan Museum of Art," *Met. Mus. Bull.*, old series 1 (1906):37; *Met. Mus. Bull.*, old series 5 (1910):289.

GIFT OF MRS. JOHN QUINCY ADAMS WARD, 1910.

William Shakespeare 17.90.2

A small study for the bronze Shakespeare monument in Central Park.

Bronze, height 27½ in. Signed: J. Q. A. Ward Sc. Dated 1870. Founder's mark: Gorham Co. Founders.

REFERENCE: *Shakespeare: Ward's Statue in Central Park New York* (1873).

EXHIBITED: Pennsylvania Academy of the Fine Arts, Philadelphia, 1894; Architectural League, New York, 1909; Panama Pacific Exposition, San Francisco, 1915.

PURCHASE, ROGERS FUND, 1917.

Horse 17.90.3

A small study for the horse designed for the equestrian statue of Major General George H. Thomas, erected in Washington in 1878.

Bronze, height 19½ in. Signed: J. Q. A. Ward. Founder's mark: Jno. Williams Inc. N. Y.

PURCHASE, ROGERS FUND, 1917.

10.200

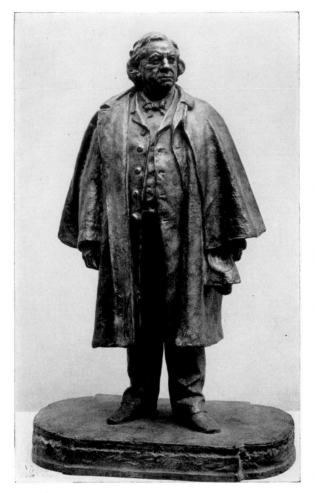

17.90.4

Henry Ward Beecher 17.90.4

This statuette of Henry Ward Beecher (1813–1887), American clergyman, orator, and author, is a study for the Beecher monument erected in Borough Hall Square, Brooklyn, New York, in 1891. The face was modeled after a death mask taken by Ward.

Bronze, height 14½ in. Signed: J. Q. A. Ward. Founder's mark: Gorham Co. Founders.

Exhibited: Architectural League, New York, 1909; Panama Pacific Exposition, San Francisco, 1915.

Purchase, Rogers Fund, 1917.

Launt Thompson
1833–1894

Born in Abbeyleix, Ireland; died in Middletown, New York. Thompson came to the United States with his widowed mother in 1847 and settled in Albany, New York. His career as a sculptor began when he was induced to lay aside his medical and anatomical studies to enter the studio of Erastus Dow Palmer (see p. 16), where he was an apprentice with Charles Calverley (see p. 33). Thompson worked as Palmer's assistant for nine years in Albany. In 1858 he opened his own studio in New York City, where he made medallion portraits and cameos. In 1859 he was made an Associate of the National Academy of Design, and in 1862 he was elected an Academician. His ready wit and great personal charm won him many friends, and for a time he had as a pupil and friend the young William Waldorf Astor. He married Marie L. Potter, sister of the famous Episcopal Bishop Henry Codman Potter. Through these connections he moved with ease into what were then termed the very highest social circles. In 1868 he went to Rome for two years and in 1875 to Florence for six years. On Thompson's return to the United States in 1881 his friends noted a marked change in his character; he was able to do little work as a sculptor because of his habit of disappearing for weeks at a time, during which he wandered in the slums of New York on drunken sprees. In 1890 his condition was so serious that he had to be committed to a private sanatorium, and in 1892 he was transferred to the State Hospital for the Insane at Middletown, New York, where he died of paresis and cancer of the throat.

His principal works are the statues of General John Sedgewick, at West Point, New York; General Winfield Scott and Admiral Dupont, in Washington; Abraham Pierson, at Yale; Napoleon I, in Milford, Pennsylvania; The Color-Bearer, in Pittsfield, Massachusetts; General Burnside, in Providence, Rhode Island; and a bust of Edwin Booth as Hamlet.

Most of Thompson's Civil War monuments are in the heavy-handed, cast-iron, realistic style that prevailed between 1865 and 1895. His earlier works in marble, especially his portrait busts and medallions, were executed in the classic cameo style of his master Palmer.

William Cullen Bryant   o.l.88.iv

William Cullen Bryant (1794–1878), American poet and editor. This bust was made in colossal size for erection on a monument that was to have been situated in Bryant Park.

Bronze, height 46½ in. Signed: L. Thompson. Dated Oct. 1 '67. Founder's mark: Bronze by L. A. Amouroux N. Y.

EXHIBITED: National Academy of Design, New York, *Annual Exhibition*, 1865, no. 632 (listed in cat. as "Wm. Cullen Bryant study for colossal bust for Central Park. Owner, C. H. Ludington.")

DEPOSITED IN THE MUSEUM BY THE NEW YORK CITY DEPARTMENT OF PUBLIC PARKS, 1896.

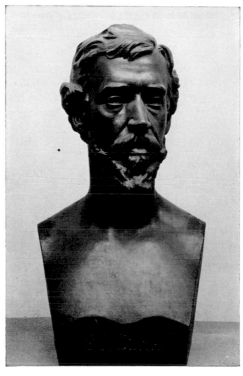

02.11.1

Charles Loring Elliott   90.17

Bust of Charles Loring Elliott (1812–1868), American portrait painter. The Museum has three other portraits of Elliott, a marble medallion by Charles Calverley (see p. 34), an oil painting by Seymour J. Guy, and a self-portrait in oil.

Marble, height 25 in. Signed: L. Thompson Sc. Dated 1870. Inscribed: Chas. L. Elliott. N. A.

REFERENCE: *Catalogue of Sculpture* (Metropolitan Museum, 1908).

GIFT OF SAMUEL P. AVERY, 1890.

Sanford R. Gifford   02.11.1

Bust of Sanford R. Gifford (1823–1880), American landscape painter. The Museum has another portrait of Gifford, an oil painting by Eastman Johnson.

Bronze, height 22¼ in. Signed: Launt Thompson Sc. Dated 1871. Inscribed: S. R. Gifford. Founder's mark: E. Henry & Bonnard Founders.

REPLICA: Century Association, New York.

REFERENCE: *Catalogue of Sculpture* (Metropolitan Museum, 1908).

EXHIBITED: National Academy of Design, New York, 1872.

GIFT OF MRS. RICHARD BUTLER, 1902.

Charles Calverley

1833–1914

BORN in Albany, New York; died in Essex Fells, New Jersey. The Museum Archives contain two autobiographical letters from Calverley, received in 1892 and 1903. "There is not much of interest to be told," he said, "as my life has been a quiet one with no romance in it—only an effort to earn a living—and trying to do as good work as I was able to do—and always endeavoring to do better work than the last—and in youth when my daily imployment didn't furnish the kind of work I liked I would satisfy my wants by doing such work at *home* as I did like to do—using such time as I could get before breakfast and after supper —and all holidays—such work was my recreation and amusement. This work seldom brought me any money—that was not the object—the *fun* of doing the things was all the reward I looked for—and I have never quite gotten over this ambition—much to the detriment of my bank account."

"Was bound in the old fashioned way for seven years to the marble cutting trade—in a one horse marble shop—this was in 1846 on my 13th birth day—and the first job I was set to do was to clean out the stove and make a fire—and my salary for the first year was one dollar a week, and found [maintained] myself (that is my mother fed and clothed me).

"After serving six years and four months of my time I was released for a consideration (money) from serving the balance of my time. Then I commenced to work for E. D. Palmer

the Albany sculptor [who had paid for his release from apprenticeship]. This was in the spring of 1853—and I continued in his service as a marble worker for fifteen years till I moved to New York—November 1868. During these years I modeled many portrait medallions of members of my family and friends —this work was all done at home and filled up all my spare time. My first medallion was a portrait of my mother.

"I opened a studio in New York City in the Fall of 1868—as a portrait sculptor—of busts and medallions—and my only deviation from that line of work was the Burns Monument at Albany—this was my first and only Statue up to date (1892)."

In his second letter Calverley gives much the same information, adding the following:

About his early medallions: "I victimized at least 40 persons during these years. I had the fun of modeling them, and they got the results."

"Since coming to New York I have probably done over 250 pieces [of] work. Busts, Medallions, Tablets and 2 Statues.

"I finished all my own marble work, and pointed much of it.

"Was elected an Associate of the National Academy of Design in 1874, and a full member in 1875."

94.13.1

Charles Loring Elliott   94.13.1

A medallion showing the profile in relief of Charles Loring Elliott (1812–1868), the American portrait painter.

Marble, height 14 in., width 12 in. (framed in ebonized wood shadow box with light blue cove mat and gilt liner). Signed: C. Calverley. Dated (on back) 1868.

REFERENCE: *Catalogue of Sculpture* (Metropolitan Museum, 1908).

EXHIBITED: National Academy of Design, New York, 1868.

GIFT OF CHARLES CALVERLEY, 1894.

Little Ida 94.13.2

Profile portrait in relief of a young Negro girl, probably made about 1871.

Marble, height 17 in., width 13¼ in. (framed in ebonized wood shadow box with light blue cove mat and gilt liner). Signed: C. Calverley. Sc.

REFERENCE: *Catalogue of Sculpture* (Metropolitan Museum, 1908).

EXHIBITED: National Academy of Design, New York, 1871, 1900.

GIFT OF CHARLES CALVERLEY, 1894.

Robert Burns 91.13

Bust of the Scottish poet Burns (1759–1796), commissioned by Andrew Carnegie.

Bronze, height 26⅞ in. Signed: Chas. Calverley Sc. Dated 1890. Founder's mark: Cast by the Henry-Bonnard Bronze Co. New York 1891.

REPLICA: Collection of Andrew Carnegie, New York.

REFERENCE: *Catalogue of Sculpture* (Metropolitan Museum, 1908).

GIFT OF ANDREW CARNEGIE, 1891.

Edward C. Moore 94.28

This bust of Edward C. Moore (1827–1891), American silversmith, art collector, and Benefactor of the Metropolitan Museum, was probably made about 1890. Moore bequeathed his collection of ceramics, glass, and metalwork and his art library to the Museum. The collection is remarkable particularly for its fine examples of Islamic glass and metalwork, but the whole collection is unusual, representing the trained tastes of a practicing designer and artist. For many years Moore was a member of the firm of jewelers and silversmiths Tiffany

94.13.2

& Company, in charge of the designing and manufacturing of silverware.

Bronze (probably cast by Tiffany & Co.), height 18 in. Signed: C. Calverley Sc. Inscribed: Edward C. Moore Born August 30th 1827 Died August 2 1891 Silversmith Artist Collector A Tribute from Friends 1894.

REFERENCES: "The Edward C. Moore Collection," *The Collector* (May 1, 1892); "The Edward C. Moore Collection," *Met. Mus. Bull.*, old series 2 (1907):105.

GIFT OF CHARLES T. COOK AND OTHERS, 1894.

Other Works

96.15. Portrait medallion of James Russell Lowell, Grolier Club Memorial. 1895. Bronze, diameter 6¾ in. Gift of the Grolier Club, 1896.

Franklin Simmons

1839–1913

BORN in Webster, Maine; died in Rome. Simmons early showed an interest in art and after working at various jobs was finally able to go to Boston, where he worked in the studio of the sculptor John Adams Jackson. Later he opened a studio of his own in Lewiston, Maine. For a time he was an itinerant artist traveling through Maine painting and modeling portraits. In Brunswick he remained to do portraits of members of the faculty of Bowdoin College and then moved on to Portland, where he executed many portrait commissions. About 1859 he received his first commission for a large statue, a monument to General Hiram G. Berry at Rockland, Maine. In 1866 Simmons was in Washington making portraits—busts and medallions—of the political and military figures there. In 1867 he went to Rome, where he remained for the rest of his life. At his death he left his estate to the Portland Art Association.

The Promised Land   97.11

A seated woman in flowing robes leaning on the stump of a palm tree.

Marble, height 63 in. Signed: Franklin Simmons. Dated: Rome, 1874. Inscribed: The Promised Land A gift from Jonathan Ackerman Coles, Columbia A.B. '64, A.M. '67, M.D. '68.

> Urbs Syon, inclyta, gloria debita glorificandis,
> Tu bona visibus interioribus intima pandis;
> Intima lumina, mentis acumina te speculantur,
> Pectora flammea spe modo, postea sorte
>   locrantur.

> Urbs Coelestis Syon. Bernardus Cluniacensis
>   A.D. 1145.

> O, illustrious name, Zion, highest in fame,
> Whose glory is that to the glorified owing,
> Thou dost knowledge dispense to the innermost
>   sense,
> Thy innermost good thus secretly showing,

> My innermost eyes, thus piercing the skies,
> From the mind's highest peaks, delighted
>   behold thee;
> Now my breast, all on fire with hope and desire,
> Transported expects sometime to enfold thee.

Transl. by Abraham Coles.

REFERENCE: M. O. Roberts, *Executor's Sale (M. O. Roberts Collection)* (1897), item no. 180.

EX COLL. Marshall O. Roberts, New York.

GIFT OF JONATHAN ACKERMAN COLES, 1897.

George Edwin Bissell

1839–1920

BORN in New Preston, Connecticut; died in Mount Vernon, New York. In an undated letter received at the Museum about 1903, the sculptor gives the following account of himself. "Educated at the Northville Academy and Gunnery, Dr. Gunn's Academy Washington, Conn. Clerk in store, Waterbury, Conn. A soldier and paymaster U.S.N., war of the Rebellion. Studied Art, English Academy, Rome.—Julian and Colorossa [Colarossi] Academies and Arts Decoratif, Paris, under Professors Aime Millet and Tabar, and anatomy at ecole de Beaux Arts, Prof. Dubois." The letter also lists twelve "principal works" done between 1883 and 1899. After the Civil War Bissell worked in his father's marble yard in Poughkeepsie, New York. He was married in 1865. In 1875 he set out to study in Europe. At various periods between 1884 and 1896 he maintained studios in Paris, where he made a number of monuments; from 1903 to 1909 he had a studio in Florence working with the sculptor Larkin G. Mead. Bissell's home, from the time of his marriage, was in Mount Vernon, New York.

Mary Justina de Peyster   07.113

This bust of Mrs. de Peyster (1802–1821) was given to the Museum by her son, John Watts de Peyster. It was probably made from a painted portrait about 1886 while Bissell was

07.113

in Poughkeepsie working for General de Peyster on monuments of his grandfather John Watts (in Trinity Churchyard) and his ancestor Abraham de Peyster (in Bowling Green). (See following entry and portrait bust of John Watts by R. B. Hughes.)

Marble, height 26½ in. Signed: Geo. E. Bissell. Inscribed: (in cartouche at front) Mary Justina de Peyster daughter of John and Jane Watts; (at back) John Watts de Peyster, her only child concepit. Died July 28th 1821. Aged 19 years 10 months and two days.

REFERENCE: Frank Allaben, *John Watts de Peyster* (1908) (contains genealogies of the Watts and de Peyster families).

GIFT OF GENERAL JOHN WATTS DE PEYSTER, 1907.

Abraham de Peyster 06.983

Abraham de Peyster (1657–1728), Dutch merchant and official, was born in New Amsterdam. This statuette is a small study for the large monument raised to the memory of his ancestor by John Watts de Peyster in the Bowling Green, New York City, in 1896.

Bronze, height 28 in. Signed: Geo. E. Bissell, Sculptor. Dated 1893. Founder's mark: Fond. G. Vignali Firenze.

REFERENCES: *Catalogue of Sculpture* (Metropolitan Museum, 1908); *Works of Art Belonging to the City of New York* (1909).

EXHIBITED: Architectural League, New York, 1893 (bronze study); Paris, Salon of 1896 (study or monument?); Museum of the City of New York, from 1948.

GIFT OF GENERAL JOHN WATTS DE PEYSTER, 1906.

Ames Van Wart

Ames Van Wart lived in France for many years and is believed to have died there in 1927. He exhibited marble portrait busts in the Paris Salons of 1904 and 1905. In the Salon catalogues he was listed as a pupil of Hiram Powers. He was a member of the Century Association from 1870 to 1927.

Marshall Owen Roberts 27.132

Bust of Marshall Owen Roberts (1814–1880), American capitalist, politician, and art collector. Roberts was Vice-President of the Board of Trustees of the Metropolitan Museum in 1870 and 1871.

Marble, height 29 in. Signed: Ames Van Wart Sc. Dated 1884.

GIFT OF CAPTAIN MARSHALL O. ROBERTS, 1927.

Pierce Francis Connelly

1841–after 1902

BORN in Grand Coteau, Louisiana. Connelly was the son of an Episcopal clergyman; both his parents became Catholic converts, and his mother founded the Order of the Holy Child Jesus. Educated in England, Connelly studied art in Paris and later studied sculpture as a pupil of Hiram Powers in Florence, where he spent most of his later life. In 1871 he exhibited two portrait busts in the Royal Academy in London. He returned to the United States in 1876 to exhibit eleven of his sculptural works at the Centennial Exposition in Philadelphia, where they were received with great acclaim. The following year he is reported to have been in New Zealand exhibiting his water-color sketches of the local scenery in Auckland. Connelly was again in Florence in 1883 at the time of his father's death. From this time on his career is quite obscure. The Museum has a note received from him in 1902, in answer to a request for biographical information. It is written in a clear, firm hand and reads in its entirety, "Pierce Francis Connelly Born 1841. in Louisiana U.S.A. (Father and Mother both born in America)." A letter from the sculptor Thomas Ball, also in the Museum's Archives, makes this comment on Connelly: "He was always rather eccentric, and for that reason I saw less of him than I would have otherwise."

Thetis and Achilles   77.2

Thetis, a sea goddess who married a mortal, Peleus, was the mother of Achilles. This work was exhibited at the Centennial Exposition in Philadelphia in 1876 with the title Thetis Thinking How She May Regain the Birthright of Her Son Achilles.

Marble, height 56 in. Signed: P. F. Connelly fecit. Dated: Flor.[ence] 1874.

REFERENCE: *International Exhibition 1876, Official Catalogue*, part II (Philadelphia, 1876).

EXHIBITED: Centennial Exposition, Philadelphia, 1876 (listed in catalogue as owned by "New York Museum").

GIFT OF MRS. A. E. SCHERMERHORN, 1877.

Preston Powers

1843–1904

BORN and died in Florence. Preston Powers, son of Hiram Powers, was trained as a mechanical draftsman in the railroad repair shops in Florence and was employed by the Grant Locomotive Works in Paris and in New Jersey. He was in the United States Navy as captain's clerk and interpreter on the U.S.S. *Canandaigua*. He became a pupil of his father in 1868. Preston Powers' principal works were portrait busts. He exhibited a bust of Evangeline in the Royal Academy in 1882 and a group called The Closing Era at the World's Columbian Exposition in Chicago in 1893, which is now in the Capitol grounds in Denver, Colorado. He spent several years in the United States. Preston Powers was named after his father's patron William C. Preston, senator from South Carolina.

Job M. Nash   92.7

According to the statement of Job M. Nash, presumably a Cincinnati merchant, in offering this bust to the Museum, it was the wish of the sculptor to have his work exhibited beside his father's bust of Jackson.

Marble, height 32½ in. Signed: Preston Powers, Sculp. Dated 1884.

REPLICA: A replica was made for Mr. Nash's tombstone in 1894.

REFERENCE: *Catalogue of Sculpture* (Metropolitan Museum, 1908).

GIFT OF JOB M. NASH, 1892.

Edward Kemeys

1843–1907

BORN in Savannah, Georgia; died in Washington, D. C. Kemeys spent his youth in New York City and was educated in the public schools there. In a letter addressed to the Museum in 1902 he states: "I never studied under any master here; no man can ever say that he gave me a lesson. Of honors I have only two, World's Fair Medals. I could have had plenty of others had I cared to mix with men, but you know, and all artists know I have always been a hermit. I cannot give a list of my works as they are in the hundreds. . . ."

Kemeys' career as a sculptor did not begin until about 1871. He had served in the Union Army all through the Civil War, had made an attempt to run a farm in Illinois, and had finally drifted to New York, where he was employed felling trees in Central Park. A great deal of his spare time was spent at the Central Park Zoo; he was fascinated by the animals. By chance one day he saw someone modeling a wolf's head and decided to try his hand as a sculptor. His first work, The Hudson

Bay Wolves, was so successful that it was bought by the Fairmount Park Commission and erected in Philadelphia in 1872. The rest of Kemeys' life was given to the study of American wild animals, and pursuing them like a hunter, he wandered all over the Western territories and states. In 1877 he went to Paris to study sculpture. But after the freedom of the Western plains Paris seemed confining, and French animal sculpture paltry, lifeless, and tame. For some years Kemeys lived in Chicago, making trips into the far West every summer. Finally he settled in Washington, D. C., where he remained to the end of his life. If not the first, he was one of the first American sculptors to turn his attention exclusively to the study of animals. In the season of 1896–1897 he gave a series of lectures called *Art and Inspiration of Mountains and Plains* and appeared before his audiences clad in the fringed and beaded buckskin costume of a frontier scout. At this time he was considered the only great animal sculptor of his time.

A Panther and Cubs 07.81

Cast in bronze from the original plaster in 1907 specially for the Museum.

Bronze, height 26½ in. Signed: Edward Kemeys. Dated 1907. Founder's mark: Jno Williams Bronze Foundry N.Y.

REPLICA: Corcoran Gallery of Art, Washington.

REFERENCE: *Catalogue of Sculpture* (Metropolitan Museum, 1908).

EXHIBITED: World's Columbian Exposition, Chicago, 1893; National Sculpture Society, Baltimore, 1908.

PURCHASE, ROGERS FUND, 1907.

A Jaguar   18.80

Bronze, height 12½ in. Signed: E. Kemeys, marked with his totem of wolf head in circle and the word Original. Inscribed: Souvenir from E. M. C. April 13 1885.

GIFT OF MRS. JAMES P. PAULDING, 1918.

Olin Levi Warner
1844–1896

BORN in Suffield, Connecticut; died in New York. Warner was the son of a Methodist minister. His childhood was spent in Amsterdam, New York, and his youth in Brandon, Vermont. At an early age he became interested in drawing and modeling, and when he was nineteen he carved a portrait bust of his father from a block of plaster. He had no special training in art until at the age of twenty-five he went to Paris on a trip paid for with savings he had earned as a railroad telegrapher. At the École des Beaux-Arts he entered the atelier of Jouffroy, where he became the friend of Augustus Saint-Gaudens, who had arrived in Paris only a few months before. Here he also knew Carpeaux, who invited him to become his studio assistant, and Falguière and Mercié. In 1872 Warner returned to the United States and opened a studio in New York, where he struggled with poverty and lack of appreciation, designing bronze gas fixtures and silverware to earn a

living. Finally he was forced to return to his father's farm. Back in New York for another attempt at the career of sculptor, he became a member of the newly formed Society of American Artists, started by Saint-Gaudens. Through this connection he won some commissions for portraits and the commission for two bronze doors for the Library of Congress. He died just when he was beginning to gain wider recognition. His friends in the National Sculpture Society arranged a memorial exhibition of his work and at its close presented four bronze medallion portraits, six portrait busts, and one figure to the Metropolitan Museum. Warner designed the souvenir half-dollar for the World's Columbian Exposition in 1893. He was a member of the National Academy of Design, the National Sculpture Society, the Society of American Artists, and the Architectural League of New York.

Thomas Fenton   98.5.2

A medallion portrait.

Bronze, diameter 7 in. Signed: O. L. Warner. Dated: N.Y. 1878. Founder's mark: Tiffany & Co.

EXHIBITED: Architectural League, New York, 1897; National Sculpture Society, New York, 1898.

GIFT OF THE NATIONAL SCULPTURE SOCIETY, 1898.

The Sculptor's Father and Mother
                                                            98.5.3
A medallion portrait.

Bronze, diameter 10½ in. Signed: O. L. Warner. Dated 1879. Inscribed: To my Father and Mother.

REFERENCE: H. Eckford, *The Century Magazine*, 37 (1889):392.

EXHIBITED: Architectural League, New York, 1897; National Sculpture Society, New York, 1898.

GIFT OF THE NATIONAL SCULPTURE SOCIETY, 1898.

Twilight 15.48

A draped standing female figure.

Marble, height 34½ in. Signed: O. L. Warner. Dated 1879.

REFERENCE: H. Eckford, *The Century Magazine*, 37 (1889):392.

EXHIBITED: Pennsylvania Academy of the Fine Arts, Philadelphia, 1899.

EX COLL. Ichabod T. Williams, New York.

PURCHASE, ROGERS FUND, 1915.

Julian Alden Weir 98.9.2

Head of Julian Alden Weir (1852–1919), American painter. This copy was specially cast for presentation to the Museum in 1898.

Bronze, height 22½ in. Signed: L. Warner. Dated 1880. Copyrighted; founder's mark: Tiffany & Co.

REPLICAS: Collection of Charles Erskine Scott Wood, Portland, Oregon, 1915; Century Association, New York.

REFERENCES: H. Eckford, *The Century Magazine*, 37 (1889):392; *Catalogue of Sculpture* (Metropolitan Museum, 1908).

EXHIBITED: Society of American Artists, New York, 1880; Paris, Salon of 1881; National Academy of Design, New York, 1888; Exposition Universelle, Paris, 1889; World's Columbian Exposition, Chicago, 1893; Architectural League, New York, 1897; National Sculpture Society, New York, 1898; Pennsylvania Academy of the Fine Arts, Philadelphia, 1899.

GIFT OF THE NATIONAL SCULPTURE SOCIETY, 1898.

Maud Morgan 98.9.3

Head of Maud Morgan (1861–1941), American musician, harpist, teacher, and author. Eckford wrote, "The sculptor appeared to wish to show that he was a master of the feminine face as well as the masculine, and could combine dignity and simplicity with beauty in one rounded piece of art. A lovely grace bathed this figure with a charm that literally and without exaggeration recalled the great antiques."

This copy was cast in bronze specially for presentation to the Museum.

Bronze, height 22¾ in. Dated 1880. Copyrighted; founder's mark: Tiffany & Co.

REPLICAS: Collection of Charles Erskine Scott Wood, Portland, Oregon, 1915; Boston Museum of Fine Arts (plaster).

REFERENCES: H. Eckford, *The Century Magazine*, 37 (1889):392; *Catalogue of Sculpture* (Metropolitan Museum, 1908).

EXHIBITED: Boston Museum of Fine Arts, 1880; Architectural League, New York, 1897; National Sculpture Society, New York, 1898; Pennsylvania Academy of the Fine Arts, Philadelphia, 1899; Panama Pacific Exposition, San Francisco, 1915.

GIFT OF THE NATIONAL SCULPTURE SOCIETY, 1898.

A. Wyatt Eaton 98.5.1

Medallion of A. Wyatt Eaton (1849–1896), American painter.

Bronze, diameter 8½ in. Signed: Olin L. Warner. Dated: New York 1883. Inscribed: A. Wyatt Eaton Pictor. Founder's mark: Tiffany & Co.

REFERENCE: H. Eckford, *The Century Magazine*, 37 (1889):392.

EXHIBITED: Architectural League, New York, 1897; National Sculpture Society, New York, 1898.

GIFT OF THE NATIONAL SCULPTURE SOCIETY, 1898.

John Insley Blair 98.9.4

Bust of John Insley Blair (1802–1899), American financier, founder of the Delaware, Lackawanna, and Western Railroad. This copy was specially cast for presentation to the Museum in 1898.

Bronze, height 23½ in. Signed: O. L. Warner fecit. Dated 1883. Copyrighted.

REFERENCE: *Catalogue of Sculpture* (Metropolitan Museum, 1908).

GIFT OF THE NATIONAL SCULPTURE SOCIETY, 1898.

Diana   98.9.5

This figure of a seated nude woman was used as a design on the binding of Lorado Taft's book, *The History of American Sculpture*. The statue is somewhat damaged: half of the shaft of the arrow held by Diana is missing.

Bronze, height 23½ in. Signed: Olin L. Warner. Dated 1887. Copyrighted; founder's mark: Tiffany & Co.

REPLICA: New York art market, 1903 (marble).

REFERENCES: H. Eckford, *The Century Magazine*, 37 (1889):392; *Catalogue of Sculpture* (Metropolitan Museum, 1908).

EXHIBITED: World's Columbian Exposition, Chicago, 1893 (plaster); Architectural League, New York, 1897; Society of American Artists, New York, 1897; National Sculpture Society, New York, 1898.

GIFT OF THE NATIONAL SCULPTURE SOCIETY, 1898.

Mrs. Olin Warner   98.9.6

This copy of the bust of the sculptor's wife was cast specially for presentation to the Museum in 1898.

Bronze, height 22 in. Signed: Olin L. Warner. Dated 1887. Inscribed: To my wife. Copyrighted; founder's mark: Tiffany & Co.

REFERENCE: *Catalogue of Sculpture* (Metropolitan Museum, 1908).

EXHIBITED: National Sculpture Society, New York, 1898.

GIFT OF THE NATIONAL SCULPTURE SOCIETY, 1898.

Charles Erskine Scott Wood   98.5.4

Medallion of Charles Erskine Scott Wood (1852–1944), American poet, essayist, and author of *Heavenly Discourses* (1927).

Bronze, diameter 8 in. Signed: O. L. Warner. Dated 1891. Inscribed: To my friend C. E. S. Wood. Founder's mark: Tiffany & Co.

REPLICA: Collection of Charles Erskine Scott Wood, Portland, Oregon, 1915.

EXHIBITED: Architectural League, New York, 1897; National Sculpture Society, New York, 1898; Panama Pacific Exposition, San Francisco, 1915.

GIFT OF THE NATIONAL SCULPTURE SOCIETY, 1898.

Joseph, Chief of the
Nez Percé Indians   06.313

His Indian name, Hin-mah-toó-yah-lat-kekht, is said to mean Thunder Rolling in the Mountains. Joseph and his tribe surrendered to the superior forces of the United States Army in 1877. This medallion was taken from life in 1889.

Bronze, diameter 17½ in. Signed: Olin L. Warner. Inscribed: Joseph Hin-mah-toó-yah-lat-kekht Chief of the "Nez Percé" Indians Portland Oregon November 1889. Founder's mark: Jno Williams Founder N.Y.

06.313

REPLICAS: Twelve replicas are believed to have been made in bronze. Most of them are in private collections.

REFERENCE: C. E. S. Wood, "Famous Indians, Portraits of Some Indian Chiefs," *The Century Magazine*, 46 (1893):436.

EXHIBITED: National Academy of Design, New York, 1890; World's Columbian Exposition, Chicago, 1893; Pennsylvania Academy of the Fine Arts, Philadelphia, 1894; Architectural League, New York, 1897; Society of American Artists, New York, 1897; National Sculpture Society, New York, 1898; Panama Pacific Exposition, San Francisco, 1915.

GIFT OF MR. AND MRS. FREDERICK S. WAIT, 1906.

N-Che-Askwe, Chief of the Coeur d'Alêne Indians   06.314

His Indian name is said to mean Old Man with the Staff. He was also known as Vincent and as Barsa. At the time this medallion was modeled he was thought to be about a hundred years old.

Bronze, diameter 7¼ in. Signed: Olin L. Warner Sc. Dated 1891. Inscribed: N-Che-Askwe Chief of the Coeur d'Alenes I.

REPLICAS: Six bronze replicas are believed to have been made.

REFERENCE: C. E. S. Wood, "Famous Indians, Portraits of Some Indian Chiefs," *The Century Magazine*, 46 (1893):436.

EXHIBITED: Architectural League, New York, 1897; National Sculpture Society, New York, 1898; Panama Pacific Exposition, San Francisco, 1915.

GIFT OF MR. AND MRS. FREDERICK S. WAIT, 1906.

Seltice, Chief of the Coeur d'Alêne Indians   06.315

A medallion portrait.

Bronze, diameter 7¼ in. Signed: Olin L. Warner, Sc. Dated 1891. Inscribed: Seltice Chief of the Coeur d'Alenes II.

REPLICAS: Six bronze replicas are believed to have been cast.

REFERENCE: C. E. S. Wood, "Famous Indians, Portraits of Some Indian Chiefs," *The Century Magazine*, 46 (1893):436.

EXHIBITED: Architectural League, New York, 1897; National Sculpture Society, New York, 1898; Panama Pacific Exposition, San Francisco, 1915.

GIFT OF MR. AND MRS. FREDERICK S. WAIT, 1906.

Moses, Chief of the Okinokan Indians   06.316

His Indian name, Sulk-Tash-Kosha, is said to mean The Half Sun.

Bronze, diameter 8¼ in. Signed: Olin L. Warner, Sc. Dated 1891. Inscribed: "Moses" Sulk-Tash-Kosha "The Half Sun" Chief of the Okinokans.

REPLICAS: Six bronze replicas are believed to have been made.

REFERENCE: C. E. S. Wood, "Famous Indians, Portraits of Some Indian Chiefs," *The Century Magazine*, 46 (1893):436.

EXHIBITED: Architectural League, New York, 1897; National Sculpture Society, New York, 1898; Panama Pacific Exposition, San Francisco, 1915.

GIFT OF MR. AND MRS. FREDERICK S. WAIT, 1906.

Ya-Tin-Ee-Ah-Witz, Chief of the Cayuse Indians   06.317

His Indian name is said to mean Poor Crane.

Bronze, diameter 10¾ in. Signed: O. L. Warner Sculpt. Dated: Umatilla, 1891. Inscribed: Ya-Tin-Ee-Ah-Witz "Poor Crane" Chief of the Cayuses A Mighty Warrior— Friend to the Whites—Thrice Wounded for

06.317

Them—He Slew Ehegant Hostile Chief—1878 Yakima War 1855—Piute 1867—Bannock & Piute 1878—Snake 1879.

REPLICAS: Six bronze replicas are believed to have been made.

REFERENCE: C. E. S. Wood, "Famous Indians, Portraits of Some Indian Chiefs," *The Century Magazine*, 46 (1893):436.

EXHIBITED: Architectural League, New York, 1897; National Sculpture Society, New York, 1898; Panama Pacific Exposition, San Francisco, 1915.

GIFT OF MR. AND MRS. FREDERICK S. WAIT, 1906.

Lot, Chief of the Spokane Indians   06.318

Bronze, diameter 8 in. Signed: O. L. Warner. Dated 1891. Inscribed: "Lot" Chief of the Spokanes.

REPLICAS: Six bronze replicas are believed to have been made.

REFERENCE: C. E. S. Wood, "Famous Indians, Portraits of Some Indian Chiefs," *The Century Magazine*, 46 (1893):436.

EXHIBITED: Architectural League, New York,

1897; National Sculpture Society, New York, 1898; Panama Pacific Exposition, San Francisco, 1915.

GIFT OF MR. AND MRS. FREDERICK S. WAIT, 1906.

Young Chief, Chief of the Cayuse Indians   06.319

Bronze, diameter 8 in. Signed: Olin L. Warner. Dated: Umatilla, 1891. Inscribed: "Young Chief" Cayuse Indian.

REPLICAS: Six bronze casts are believed to have been made.

REFERENCE: C. E. S. Wood, "Famous Indians, Portraits of Some Indian Chiefs," *The Century Magazine*, 46 (1893):436.

EXHIBITED: Architectural League, New York, 1897; National Sculpture Society, New York, 1898; Panama Pacific Exposition, San Francisco, 1915.

GIFT OF MR. AND MRS. FREDERICK S. WAIT, 1906.

Sabine, Daughter of Kash-Kash, a Cayuse Indian   06.320

Bronze, diameter 5¾ in. Signed: O. L. Warner, Sc. Dated 1891. Inscribed: Sabine Kash-Kash's Daughter a Cayuse ae[tatis] XIV.

06.318

REPLICAS: Six bronze replicas are believed to have been made.

REFERENCE: C. E. S. Wood, "Famous Indians, Portraits of Some Indian Chiefs," *The Century Magazine* 46 (1893):436.

EXHIBITED: Architectural League, New York, 1897; National Sculpture Society, New York, 1898; Panama Pacific Exposition, San Francisco, 1915.

GIFT OF MR. AND MRS. FREDERICK S. WAIT, 1906.

William Rudolph O'Donovan

1844–1920

BORN in Preston County, Virginia (now part of West Virginia); died in New York. At the age of eighteen O'Donovan joined the Confederate Army and served throughout the Civil War. He appears to have been entirely self-taught as a painter and sculptor. About 1874 O'Donovan settled in New York City, where he became known for his realistic portrait busts. Many of them were portraits of artists such as William Page, Winslow Homer, and Thomas Eakins. He is perhaps best remembered today for his work in collaboration with Eakins in making the high relief equestrian portraits of Lincoln and Grant for the Soldiers and Sailors Memorial in Prospect Park Plaza, Brooklyn. O'Donovan was one of the founding members of the Tile Club (1877). Many of his landscape paintings were made in the vicinity of Rye, New York, where he spent his summer holidays. O'Donovan also made portrait busts of Walt Whitman and the less well-known poet Clarence Edmund Stedman, as well as three monuments to George Washington in Caracas, Venezuela, Trenton, New Jersey, and Newburgh, New York.

Winslow Homer 23.83

Bust of the American artist Homer (1836–1910), made before 1900.

Bronze, height 12 in. Signed: O'Donovan. Dated N Y 18— (illegible). Copyrighted; founder's mark: Roman Bronze Works N.Y.

PURCHASE, ROGERS FUND, 1923.

Augustus Saint-Gaudens

1848–1907

BORN in Dublin; died in Cornish, New Hampshire. Augustus Saint-Gaudens was brought to the United States as an infant. His parents settled in New York City, where he received a public school education. At the age of thirteen he was apprenticed to a cameo-cutter. He attended classes in drawing at Cooper Union and at the National Academy of Design. At the age of nineteen he went to Paris, where he studied at the École des Beaux-Arts and worked in the atelier of the sculptor François Jouffroy. In 1870 he went to Rome. There he met some traveling Americans who gave him commissions and introduced him to other prospective patrons. Shortly after his return to the United States in 1875, he received commissions for two statues—the monument to Admiral Farragut, now in Madison Square, New York, and the statue of Robert R. Randall. The unveiling of the Farragut monument in 1881 established his reputation, and from that time forward he was considered the leading American sculptor. Among his more famous works are Diana (now in the Philadelphia Museum of Art), the Shaw Memorial in Boston, the memorial to Mrs. Henry Adams in Rock Creek Cemetery in Washington, and the monument to General Sherman in Central Park, New York.

He was showered with honors, commissions, and praise, as the most important figure of the American art world in the final decades of the nineteenth century. His influence and example inspired most of the younger sculptors of the period. More has been written about Saint-Gaudens, his work, and his place in the history of American sculpture than about any other sculptor of the time, and he engaged the active interest and support of almost all of the major critics. He often worked in collaboration with the architects Stanford White and Charles McKim and the designer John La Farge on some of their larger projects. He died at his studio in Cornish, New Hampshire.

Francis Davis Millet   10.223

Relief portrait of Francis Davis Millet (1846–1912) American painter, mural decorator, and illustrator.

Bronze, height 10½ in., width 6¾ in. Signed: Augustus Saint-Gaudens Fecit. Inscribed: Francis Davis Millet Aetatis Suae XXXII Paris March MDCCCLXXIX. Copyrighted.

REPLICAS: Private collection, New York; Boston Museum of Fine Arts.

REFERENCE: C. L. Hind, *Augustus Saint-Gaudens* (1908).

EXHIBITED: Boston Museum of Fine Arts, 1880.

GIFT OF MRS. F. W. ADLARD, 1910.

12.76.3

Admiral David Glasgow Farragut
12.76.3

This head of Admiral Farragut (1801–1870) was cast for the Museum in 1910 from the study made in Paris in 1879 and 1880 for the Farragut Monument, which was unveiled in Madison Square in 1881. The unveiling of this statue was considered as marking the beginning of a new epoch in American sculpture and the decorative arts because of the importance of the pedestal designed by Stanford White.

Bronze, height 11¼ in. Signed: A St G (monogram). Inscribed: Copyright by Augusta H. Saint-Gaudens MCMVIII. Founder's mark: Aubry Bros. Founders N Y.

REPLICA: Saint-Gaudens Memorial, Cornish, New Hampshire.

REFERENCES: H. Saint-Gaudens, *Reminiscences of Augustus Saint-Gaudens* (1913); C. Baldwin, *Stanford White* (1930).

EXHIBITED: Paris, Salon of 1880 (plaster statue), Honorable Mention; Metropolitan Museum, memorial exhibition, 1908; John Herron Art Institute, Indianapolis, 1909; Detroit Institute of Arts, 1915.

GIFT BY SUBSCRIPTION THROUGH THE SAINT-GAUDENS REPLICA COMMITTEE, 1912.

Jules Bastien-Lepage   12.76.4

Relief portrait of Jules Bastien-Lepage (1848–1884), French artist. In his *Reminiscences* Saint-Gaudens said of this work: "Then [1879] I met Bastien-Lepage, who was in the height of the renown he had achieved by his painting of Joan of Arc. This picture Mr. Irwin Davis subsequently purchased and, at my earnest recommendation, gave to the Metropolitan Museum of Art. Lepage was short, bullet-headed, athletic and in comparison to the majority of my friends, dandified in dress. I recall his having been at the Beaux-Arts during the period I studied there, and my disliking him for his general cockiness. He asked if I would make a medallion of him in exchange for a

portrait of myself. Of course I agreed to the proposal, and as his studio was not far from mine, the medallion was modeled during a period when he was unable to work on account of a sprained ankle. He moved away shortly afterward, and I saw little of him except for the four hours a day when I posed for the full-length sketch he made of me. This painting was destroyed in the fire which burned my studio in 1904." Homer Saint-Gaudens remarked of this medallion: "None of the medallions my father then modeled satisfied him to the extent of that of Bastien-Lepage, both because he believed the relief was as near perfection as he ever came, and because he was greatly interested in a rare combination of talent and vanity in his sitter."

Bronze, height 14½ in., width 10½ in. Inscribed: Jules Bastien-Lepage Aetatis xxxi Paris MDCCCLXXX Augustus Saint-Gaudens Fecit.

REPLICAS: Musée du Luxembourg, Paris (bronze reduction); Saint-Gaudens Memorial, Cornish, New Hampshire; Brooklyn Museum, New York; City Art Museum, St. Louis; Detroit Institute of Arts; Boston Museum of Fine Arts; Art Institute of Chicago.

REFERENCE: H. Saint-Gaudens, *Reminiscences of Augustus Saint-Gaudens* (1913).

EXHIBITED: Boston Museum of Fine Arts, 1880; Cincinnati Art Museum, 1902; Metropolitan Museum, memorial exhibition (cat.), 1908; John Herron Art Institute, Indianapolis, 1909; Detroit Institute of Arts, 1915.

GIFT BY SUBSCRIPTION THROUGH THE SAINT-GAUDENS REPLICA COMMITTEE, 1912.

The Children of Prescott Hall Butler
05.15.1

Relief portrait of Lawrence Smith Butler and Charles Stewart Butler, two little boys dressed in Scottish Highland costume. Prescott Hall Butler was a prominent New York lawyer and the brother-in-law of the architect Stanford White. This work inspired the poet George

Worthington to write his verses "A Bas-Relief by Saint-Gaudens."

This copy was cut in marble from the original plaster in 1907 at Piccirilli Studios.

Marble, height 24½ in., width 35½ in. Signed: A St G (monogram) fecit. Inscribed: (at upper left, an endless knot with the Latin motto repeated twice) Dabit Deus His Quoque Finem; (at left) Charles Stewart Butler in His Fourth Year; (at right) Lawrence Smith Butler in His Sixth Year; (below) To My Friend Prescott Hall Butler Sixth of July Eighteen Hundred and Eighty. March Twenty Sixth Eighteen Hundred and Eighty One. Modelled by Augustus Saint-Gaudens New York October Eighteen Hundred and Eighty March Eighteen Hundred and Eighty One. Copyrighted.

REPLICAS: Musée du Luxembourg, Paris (small bronze); private collection, New York (bronze original). A number of small bronze replicas are believed to have been made.

REFERENCES: "Augustus Saint-Gaudens — Replicas of His Bas-Reliefs of Children," *Met. Mus. Bull.*, old series 1 (1906):24; H. Saint-Gaudens, *Reminiscences of Augustus Saint-Gaudens* (1913); G. Worthington, *Art and Progress*, 4 (1913):1020; A. Adams, "Aspet," *Art and Progress*, 6 (1915):139.

EXHIBITED: Metropolitan Museum, memorial exhibition (cat.), 1908; John Herron Art Institute, Indianapolis, 1909; Detroit Institute of Arts, 1915.

GIFT OF JACOB H. SCHIFF, 1905.

Samuel Gray Ward
12.29

Relief portrait of Samuel Gray Ward, one of the Founders and first Treasurer of The Metropolitan Museum of Art, a member of the Board of Trustees of the Museum from 1870 to 1879. This was one of Saint-Gaudens's earliest portrait commissions, and one that he considered among his best works.

Bronze, height 19 in., width 13¼ in. (wood frame). Signed: A St G (monogram). Inscribed: Samuel Gray Ward New York May MDCCCLXXXI. Copyrighted.

REPLICAS: Private collection, Boston; Musée du Luxembourg, Paris (small bronze).

REFERENCE: H. Saint-Gaudens, *Reminiscences of Augustus Saint-Gaudens* (1913).

EXHIBITED: Society of American Artists, New York, 1882; Metropolitan Museum, memorial exhibition (cat.), 1908; John Herron Art Institute, Indianapolis, 1909; Detroit Institute of Arts, 1915.

GIFT OF MRS. AUGUSTUS SAINT-GAUDENS, 1912.

Homer Saint-Gaudens   05.15.2

Relief portrait of Homer Saint-Gaudens (1880–1958), the son of the sculptor. This copy was cut in marble in 1907.

Marble, height 20½ in., width 16½ in. Inscribed: To My Friend Doctor Henry Schiff This Portrait of My Son Homer Schiff Saint-Gaudens at the Age of Seventeen Months. Augustus Saint-Gaudens New York February MDCCCLXXXII. Copyrighted.

REPLICAS: Saint-Gaudens Memorial, Cornish, New Hampshire (bronze); Detroit Institute of Arts (bronze); Century Association, New York (bronze); Brooklyn Museum, New York (bronze). A number of small electrotype replicas were made, one of which is in the Musée du Luxembourg, Paris.

REFERENCE: *Saint-Gaudens Memorial Exhibition* (Metropolitan Museum, 1908).

EXHIBITED: Society of American Artists, New York, 1882; Metropolitan Museum, memorial exhibition, 1908; John Herron Art Institute, Indianapolis, 1909; Detroit Institute of Arts, 1915.

GIFT OF JACOB H. SCHIFF, 1905.

Amor Caritas   19.124

Until this design was completed, it was called The Angel with the Tablet. It was developed

from the designs made originally for the Morgan Tomb in Hartford and the Smith Tomb in Newport. This example was cast in bronze especially for the Museum in 1918.

Gilded bronze, height 102½ in., width 48 in. Signed: Augustus Saint-Gaudens. Dated MDCCCLXXX (VII). Inscribed (on tablet above head): Amor Caritas.

REPLICAS: Musée du Luxembourg, Paris; Saint-Gaudens Memorial, Cornish, New Hampshire (plaster, and bronze reduction); Detroit Institute of Arts (bronze); Art Institute of Chicago (plaster?).

REFERENCES: C. L. Hind, *Augustus Saint-Gaudens* (1908); H. Saint-Gaudens, *Reminis-*

19.124

cences of Augustus Saint-Gaudens (1913); L. Taft, *Modern Tendencies in Sculpture* (1917).

EXHIBITED: Exposition Universelle, Paris, 1900; Pan American Exposition, Buffalo, 1901; Art Institute of Chicago, 1907; Metropolitan Museum, memorial exhibition (cat.), 1908; John Herron Art Institute, Indianapolis, 1909; Detroit Institute of Arts, 1915.

PURCHASE, ROGERS FUND, 1918.

Robert Louis Stevenson   12.76.1

Relief portrait of Robert Louis Stevenson (1850–1894), English author. Stevenson posed for Saint-Gaudens in New York. The sittings were arranged by their friend the artist Will H. Low. In his *Reminiscences* Saint-Gaudens wrote: "I began the medallion at his rooms in the Hotel Albert in Eleventh Street, not far from where I lived in Washington Place. All I had time to do from him then was the head, which I modeled in five sittings of two or three hours each. These were given me in the morning, while he, as was his custom, lay in bed propped up with pillows." The studies for the hands were made later at Manasquan, New Jersey. This portrait, redrawn in a horizontal rectangle with a number of modifications in the design of the bed, a different in-

scription, and the worldly cigarette in the right hand exchanged for a quill pen, was used for the memorial plaque erected after Stevenson's death in St. Giles Cathedral in Edinburgh, Scotland. The first version of the Stevenson portrait was drawn in an upright rectangle.

At the left descending irregularly in the field is the following poem, dedicated by Stevenson to Will H. Low and published in Stevenson's volume of poems *Underwoods*, 1887:

Youth now flees on feathered foot
Faint and fainter sounds the flute
Rarer songs of gods and still
Somewhere on the sunny hill
Or along the winding stream
Through the willows flits a dream
Flits but shows a smiling face
Flees but with so quaint a grace
None can choose to stay at home
All must follow, all must roam

This is unborn beauty, she
Now in air floats high and free
Takes the sun and breaks the blue
Late with stooping pinion flew
Raking hedgerow trees and wet
Her wing in silver streams and set
Shining foot on temple roof
Now again she flies aloof
Coasting mountain clouds and kiss't
By the evening's amethyst

In wet wood and miry lane
Still we pant and pound in vain
Still with leaden foot we chase
Waning pinion, fainting face
Still with grey hair we stumble on
Till behold the vision gone
Where hath fleeting beauty led
To the doorway of the dead

Life is over, Life was gay
We have come the primrose way.

Bronze, diameter 34¾ in. (wood frame). Dated MDCCCLXXXVII. Inscribed: (at top) To Robert Louis Stevenson in His Thirty Seventh Year Augustus Saint-Gaudens; (at left) Replica made for The Metropolitan Museum of Art Aspet MCMX. Copyrighted.

12.76.1

REPLICAS: Musée du Luxembourg, Paris (small round bronze); Saint-Gaudens Memorial, Cornish, New Hampshire (round); Harvard University Library, Cambridge, Massachusetts (round); National Academy of Design, New York (round); Princeton University, Princeton, New Jersey (round); John Herron Art Institute, Indianapolis; Mr. and Mrs. Junius Fishburn, Chappaqua, New York (plaster, round). A replica was formerly in the collection of Charles Deering. A replica of the rectangular version in St. Giles Cathedral was in the Albright Art Gallery, Buffalo, in 1902.

REFERENCES: R. Cortissoz, *Augustus Saint-Gaudens* (1908); Will H. Low, *A Chronicle of Friendships* (1908); H. Saint-Gaudens, *Reminiscences of Augustus Saint-Gaudens* (1913).

EXHIBITED: Pan American Exposition, Buffalo, 1901; Pennsylvania Academy of the Fine Arts, Philadelphia, 1902; Cincinnati Art Museum, 1902; Art Institute of Chicago, 1907; Metropolitan Museum, memorial exhibition (cat.), 1908; John Herron Art Institute, Indianapolis, 1909; Detroit Institute of Arts, 1915.

GIFT BY SUBSCRIPTION THROUGH THE SAINT-GAUDENS REPLICA COMMITTEE, 1912.

The Children of Jacob H. Schiff

05.15.3

Relief portraits of a little boy and a little girl with a Scotch deerhound. Jacob H. Schiff was a prominent New York banker and philanthropist and a Benefactor of this Museum. This example was made in 1907 for the Museum. The original bronze has inscribed on it the names of the children (Leo Mortimer, Fanny Frieda), omitted here.

Marble, height 69½ in., width 51 in. Signed: Augustus Saint-Gaudens fecit. Dated MDCCC-LXXXVIII.

REPLICAS: Saint-Gaudens Memorial, Cornish, New Hampshire; private collection, New York (bronze).

REFERENCE: "Augustus Saint-Gaudens — Replicas of His Bas-Reliefs of Children," *Met Mus. Bull.*, old series 1 (1906):24.

EXHIBITED: Metropolitan Museum, memorial exhibition (cat.), 1908; John Herron Art Institute, Indianapolis, 1909; Detroit Institute of Arts, 1915.

GIFT OF JACOB H. SCHIFF, 1905.

Mariana Griswold Van Rensselaer

17.104

Relief portrait of Mrs. Schuyler Van Rensselaer (1851–1934), American art critic and author of a number of books and articles on art, including *American Etchers* (1886), *American Figure Painters* (1886), *Henry Hobson*

Richardson and His Works (1888), *Six Portraits* (1889), *English Cathedrals* (1892), and *A History of New York City in the Seventeenth Century* (1909). Many of her articles were published in *The Century Magazine*. Mrs. Van Rensselaer stated that Saint-Gaudens wanted to do her portrait because he liked her high collar. The carved oak frame for this portrait was designed by Stanford White.

Bronze, height 20¼ in., width 7¾ in. (oak frame). Inscribed: Animus Non Opus To Mariana Griswold Van Rensselaer Augustus Saint-Gaudens MDCCCLXXXVIII.

REPLICAS: Private collection, New York (?); Musée du Luxembourg, Paris (small bronze); Saint-Gaudens Memorial, Cornish, New Hampshire (small bronze).

REFERENCE: *Saint-Gaudens Memorial Exhibition* (Metropolitan Museum, 1908).

EXHIBITED: Society of American Artists, New York, 1889; Metropolitan Museum, memorial exhibition, 1908; John Herron Art Institute, Indianapolis, 1909; Detroit Institute of Arts, 1915.

GIFT OF MRS. SCHUYLER VAN RENSSELAER, 1917.

Diana   28.101

This figure of Diana, goddess of the hunt, was designed in 1892 as a weather vane for the tower of Stanford White's Madison Square Garden. Saint-Gaudens's studio assistant Oscar Lenz has been credited with doing much of the work on the figure, one of the few nudes by Saint-Gaudens. The first figure, which was eighteen feet high, when erected on the tower proved to be out of scale with the rest of the building, and was taken down and replaced by a smaller copy, thirteen feet high. The eighteen-foot Diana was then sent to Chicago for exhibition at the World's Columbian Exposition (1893), and later it was bought and placed on the tower of the Montgomery Ward Building in Chicago. When the old Madison Square Garden was demolished in 1926, the thirteen-foot Diana was salvaged and presented to the Philadelphia Museum of Art. In 1928 two more replicas of the Diana were cast in bronze in Germany in a still smaller size, about nine feet high. One of them was made specially for the Metropolitan Museum. This example lacks the flying drapery designed for the original model.

Gilded bronze, height 112 in. Copyrighted. Founder's mark: P. B. v. Co. Munich Made in Germany.

REPLICAS: Philadelphia Museum of Art (sheet copper); private collection, New York (bronze); National Art Collection, Smithsonian Institution, Washington; a replica formerly in the collection of Charles Follen McKim, New York (bronze, 42 in. high); Saint-Gaudens Memorial, Cornish, New Hampshire (bronze cast of a study for head).

28.101

REFERENCES: C. L. Hind, *Augustus Saint-Gaudens* (1908); H. Saint-Gaudens, *Reminiscences of Augustus Saint-Gaudens* (1913); C. Baldwin, *Stanford White* (1930).

EXHIBITED: World's Columbian Exposition, Chicago, 1893; Art Institute of Chicago, 1907; Metropolitan Museum, memorial exhibition (cat.), 1908; John Herron Art Institute, Indianapolis, 1910; Detroit Institute of Arts, 1915.

PURCHASE, ROGERS FUND, 1928.

The Puritan   39.65.53

A small copy of the original, which is a bronze statue in heroic size, of Deacon Samuel Chapin, at Springfield, Massachusetts, made in 1887. In 1905 a variant copy, also in heroic size, was erected in City Hall Square, Philadelphia. This has been relocated in Fairmount Park. It is not an actual portrait of Deacon Samuel Chapin.

Bronze, height 31 in. Signed: Augustus Saint Gaudens. Dated MDCCCXCIX. Inscribed: The Puritan. Copyrighted.

REPLICAS: Whitney Museum of American Art, New York (small size); Art Institute of Chicago (small size); Brookgreen Gardens, South Carolina (small size); Saint-Gaudens Memorial, Cornish, New Hampshire (small size?); University of Nebraska, Lincoln; Carnegie Institute, Pittsburgh; Springfield, Massachusetts (heroic scale); Fairmount Park, Philadelphia (heroic scale).

REFERENCES: H. Saint-Gaudens, *Reminiscences of Augustus Saint-Gaudens* (1913); L. Taft, *Modern Tendencies in Sculpture* (1917); P. Remington, "The Bequest of Jacob Ruppert," *Met. Mus. Bull.*, old series 34 (1939):169.

EXHIBITED: Pennsylvania Academy of the Fine Arts, Philadelphia, 1898, 1907; Exposition Universelle, Paris, 1900; Louisiana Purchase Exposition, St. Louis, 1904; Art Institute of Chicago, 1907; Cincinnati Art Museum, 1907; John Herron Art Institute, Indianapolis, 1909; Detroit Institute of Arts, 1915.

BEQUEST OF JACOB RUPPERT, 1939.

39.65.53

Josephine Shaw Lowell   25.89

This relief portrait of Mrs. Charles Russell Lowell (1843-1905), American philanthropist and reformer, was made in 1899.

Marble, height 12½ in., width 9 in. Signed: A St G (monogram).

REPLICA: Private collection, Boston.

REFERENCE: H. Saint-Gaudens, *Reminiscences of Augustus Saint-Gaudens* (1913).

EXHIBITED: Society of American Artists, New York, 1902; Metropolitan Museum, memorial exhibition (cat.), 1908.

GIFT OF CHARLES C. BURLINGHAM, 1925.

Louise Adele Gould   15.105.1

Relief portrait of Mrs. Charles W. Gould, dressed as a bride. This half-length portrait, made between 1884 and 1894, is modeled in a circular plaque set in a rectangular architectural frame with an ornamental cresting of acanthus scrolls in the manner of Stanford White. Charles W. Gould was a Trustee of the Metropolitan Museum from 1915 to 1931.

Marble, height 41 in., width 26½ in. Signed: Augustus Saint-Gaudens. Inscribed: (at top of circular plaque) Louise Adele Gould Saint Agnes Eve MDCCCLXXXI; (on tablet below circular plaque) She Seemed A Splendid Angel Newly Dressed Save Wings For Heaven. Copyrighted.

REFERENCE: C. L. Hind, *Augustus Saint-Gaudens* (1908).

GIFT OF CHARLES W. GOULD, 1915.

Louise Adele Gould   15.105.2

Portrait bust of Mrs. Charles W. Gould, made about 1894 or 1895 (see following entry).

Marble, height 22 in. Signed: Augustus Saint-Gaudens.

REFERENCE: C. L. Hind, *Augustus Saint-Gaudens* (1908).

GIFT OF CHARLES W. GOULD, 1915.

Louise Adele Gould   32.62.1

Made about 1904. Hind stated, "This bust was the result of studies of the same subject extending over several years, a marble relief being executed between the years 1884 and 1894, and a marble bust in the round 1894–1895." All three of these portraits are now in this Museum (see preceding entries).

Marble, height 15½ in. Signed: Augustus Saint-Gaudens. Copyrighted.

REPLICA: Cooper Union Museum, New York (wax).

REFERENCE: C. L. Hind, *Augustus Saint-Gaudens* (1908).

EXHIBITED: Metropolitan Museum, memorial exhibition (cat.), 1908.

BEQUEST OF CHARLES W. GOULD, 1932.

General William Tecumseh Sherman
12.76.2

William Tecumseh Sherman (1820–1891), Civil War general. Of this portrait Saint-Gaudens wrote in his *Reminiscences*: "While modeling the relief of the Stevenson I had in my studio another absorbing portrait, a bust of General Sherman, the chance to make which Whitelaw Reid had been instrumental in obtaining for me. This task was also a labor of love, for the General had remained in my eye as the typical American soldier ever since I had formed that idea of him during the Civil War. The bust I made in about eighteen periods of two hours each [in 1887]. It was a memorable experience, and I regret nothing more than that I did not write down a daily record of his conversation, for he talked freely and most delightfully of the war, men and things." This portrait later served as a study for the Sherman equestrian monument, unveiled in 1903 in New York. This example was cast in 1910.

Bronze, height 32½ in. Inscribed: William Tecumseh Sherman Copyright by Augustus Saint-Gaudens MDCCCXCII.

REPLICAS: Private collection, New York (1908); Saint-Gaudens Memorial, Cornish, New Hampshire; Pennsylvania Academy of the Fine Arts, Philadelphia; United States Military Academy, West Point.

REFERENCES: A. S., *Brush and Pencil*, 12 (1903):262; C. L. Hind, *Augustus Saint-Gaudens* (1908); H. Saint-Gaudens, *Reminiscences of Augustus Saint-Gaudens* (1913); L. Taft, *Modern Tendencies in Sculpture* (1917).

EXHIBITED: Philadelphia Art Club, 1890; Metropolitan Museum, memorial exhibition (cat.), 1908; John Herron Art Institute, Indianapolis, 1909; Detroit Institute of Arts, 1915.

GIFT BY SUBSCRIPTION THROUGH THE SAINT-GAUDENS REPLICA COMMITTEE, 1912.

Sherman Monument—Victory

17.90.1

Designed as part of the Sherman Monument unveiled in 1903 at Fifth Avenue and 59 Street, New York City. In various letters Saint-Gaudens wrote of this work: "I have been arranging drapery on four copies I have made of the nude of the 'Victory,' and one of the four has come remarkably well, so all I have to do is copy it, and I am consequently much elated. . . . the small 'Victory' . . . will be ready for the Salon in the spring. . . . The reason I have felt so elated over this drapery business, is that it makes the drapery on the Library figures and the Angel with the Brooks, child's play, as far as the always complicated and terrible question of how to arrange flowing draperies goes. It's a question that each fellow has to dig out for himself. I have been two weeks arranging these four models with the greatest care . . . I think I told you that my 'Victory' is getting on well. It's the grandest 'Victory' anybody ever made. Hooraah! . . . I'm very cocky about the 'Sherman,' which has turned out well, particularly the 'Victory'."

Gilded bronze, height 41¾ in. Signed: Augustus Saint-Gaudens Fecit. Dated MCMII. Copyrighted.

REPLICA: Saint-Gaudens Memorial, Cornish, New Hampshire (?).

REFERENCE: H. Saint-Gaudens, *Reminiscences of Augustus Saint-Gaudens* (1913).

EXHIBITED: Detroit Institute of Arts, 1915.

PURCHASE, ROGERS FUND, 1917.

Sherman Monument—Study for the Head of Victory

07.90

Of this head C. L. Hind remarked: "Although Saint-Gaudens had a preference for this head, he did not consider that it accorded so well with the statue [the Sherman equestrian monument] as the first study. The latter was used for the equestrian group, and the profile of this second study was later reproduced in re-

17.90.1

lief as the model for the new cent and the ten-dollar coin." In the catalogue of the Saint-Gaudens Memorial Exhibition (1908) this head is described: "Saint-Gaudens's spiritual rendering of the classic conception is, as a brother sculptor has said, 'an expression of our race and time.'"

Bronze, height 8¼ in. Signed: Augustus Saint-Gaudens. Dated MCMV. Inscribed (in Greek): Victory Peace. Copyrighted MCMVII.

REPLICAS: Private collection, Cambridge, Massachusetts; Saint-Gaudens Memorial, Cornish, New Hampshire; Newark Museum, New Jersey.

REFERENCES: C. L. Hind, *Augustus Saint-Gaudens* (1908); *Saint-Gaudens Memorial Exhibition* (Metropolitan Museum, 1908); H. Saint-Gaudens, *Reminiscences of Augustus Saint-Gaudens* (1913).

EXHIBITED: Art Institute of Chicago, 1907; Metropolitan Museum, memorial exhibition, 1908; John Herron Art Institute, Indianapolis, 1909; Detroit Institute of Arts, 1915.

PURCHASE, ROGERS FUND, 1907.

Other Works

90.18.1. Medal commemorating the centenary of Washington's inauguration as first president of the United States. 1889. Bronze, diameter 4½ in. Gift of Henry G. Marquand, 1890.

06.1192. Medal commemorating the two-hundredth anniversary of Benjamin Franklin's birth. 1906. Bronze, diameter 4 in. Gift of President Theodore Roosevelt, 1906.

08.216. Plaquette commemorating the twentieth anniversary of the founding of the Cornish Colony. 1905. Silver, 3 x 1¾ in. Gift of Kenyon Cox, 1908.

13.78. Portrait medal of John Singer Sargent. 1885. Bronze, diameter 2½ in. Gift of Mrs. Edward Robinson, 1913.

24.20. Portrait plaquette of Charles Follen McKim. Inscribed: In souvenir of the ten jolly days I passed with you and the illustrious Stanford White in the south of France. 1878. Bronze, 7⁵⁄₁₆ x 4⅞ in. Gift of Mrs. Charles D. Norton, 1924.

Frank Duveneck

1848–1919

BORN in Covington, Kentucky; died in Cincinnati. As a young man Duveneck studied painting in Cincinnati and later in Munich. His fame as an artist rests almost entirely on his work as a painter and teacher. His best-known piece of sculpture is the portrait effigy of his wife designed for her tomb. This, and a few other essays in sculpture (portraits of Ralph W. Emerson and Charles W. Eliot) were done in collaboration with the Cincinnati sculptor and wood-carver Clement H. Barnhorn. Both Duveneck and Barnhorn were teachers in the Cincinnati Art Academy for many years.

Clement J. Barnhorn was born in Cincinnati in 1857 and died there in 1935. He was the pupil of the sculptor Rebisso and the wood-carver Henry L. Fry in Cincinnati and of Puech and Mercié at the Académie Julian in Paris. Except for the years 1891 to 1895, which he spent in Paris, Barnhorn lived in Cincinnati, where he was head of the department of sculpture in the Cincinnati Art Academy until his death.

Tomb Effigy of Elizabeth Boott Duveneck   27.64

Elizabeth Boott Duveneck (d. 1888), wife of the sculptor, was also an artist. A bronze replica of this work was placed over Mrs. Duveneck's grave in the Allori Cemetery in Florence about 1895. It was designed and executed in collaboration with the sculptor Clement J. Barnhorn in Cincinnati in 1891 (plaster original is in the Cincinnati Art Museum). The number of copies to be found in American museums attests to its great popularity. This example was cast in 1927 from a plaster cast presented to the Museum in 1917 by Frank Duveneck. The plaster copy was then given by the Museum to the art gallery of the University of Nebraska.

Gilded bronze (cast by Gorham Co.), height 28½ in., length 85 in. Signed: Frank Duveneck. Dated 1891.

REPLICAS: Allori Cemetery, Florence (bronze); Boston Museum of Fine Arts (marble); Pennsylvania Academy of the Fine Arts, Philadelphia (marble); Art Institute of Chicago (marble); San Francisco Art Association (marble); John Herron Art Institute, Indianapolis (bronze); University of Nebraska Art Galleries, Lincoln (plaster).

REFERENCES: N. Herrmann, *Frank Duveneck* (1918); L. Taft, *History of American Sculpture* (1930).

EXHIBITED: Paris, Salon of 1895, Honorable Mention; National Sculpture Society, New York, 1898; Panama Pacific Exposition, San Francisco, 1915; Metropolitan Museum, 1918; Newark Museum, New Jersey, 1962.

PURCHASE, ROGERS FUND, 1927.

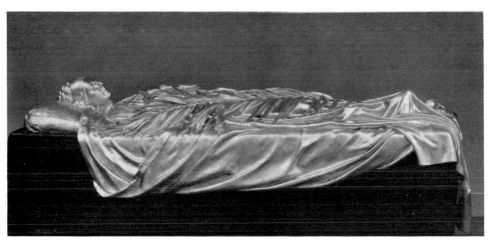

27.64

Daniel Chester French

1850–1931

BORN in Exeter, New Hampshire; died in Stockbridge, Massachusetts. French's education as a sculptor began in Concord, Massachusetts, at the age of nineteen, with some instruction from William Morris Hunt. He attended the anatomy class of William Rimmer (see p. 13) in Boston. He was encouraged in his decision to become a sculptor by his family and by Louisa May Alcott. He had the advantage of study for a month in the Brooklyn studio of John Quincy Adams Ward. Through the efforts of Ralph Waldo Emerson the town of Concord awarded him the commission for The Minute Man. Its success and its prominence as a national monument brought him immediate fame. In 1876 he went to Italy for two years of study with the Boston sculptor Thomas Ball (see p. 20). On his return to the United States he opened a studio in Washington, where his father was Assistant Secretary of the Treasury. Among his early commissions were groups of architectural sculpture for the United States Customs House in St. Louis, the Customs House in Philadelphia, and the Boston Post Office. Many of his smaller works were designed to

be reproduced in Parian ware and were similar in style to the Rogers Groups. In 1886 French went to Paris to study with Mercié and to execute a commission for the state of Michigan, a statue of General Lewis Cass, now in the Capitol in Washington. On his return he settled in New York City, where he became one of the leading figures of the art world and a member, with Augustus Saint-Gaudens, of the select artistic circle revolving around Richard Watson Gilder, poet and editor of *The Century Magazine.*

French's best known work is his statue of Abraham Lincoln in the Lincoln Memorial in Washington (1922). Perhaps his best portrait is the head of Ralph Waldo Emerson (see below) modeled from life in 1879. In 1903 French was elected a Trustee of this Museum, and until his death was chairman of the Trustees' Committee on Sculpture. The Museum's collection of modern sculpture, gathered during his incumbency, stands as a monument to his tastes and principles.

Ralph Waldo Emerson 07.101

When the sculptor was at work on this head of Emerson (1803–1882), American philosopher and author, Emerson is reported to have said, "The more it resembles me the worse it

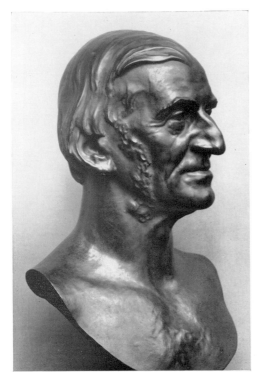

07.101

looks." When he was asked if he thought it a good likeness he said, "Yes, that is the face I shave."

Bronze, height 23 in. Signed: D. C. French. Dated 1879. Founder's mark: The Henry-Bonnard Brown Co. Mount Vernon N.Y.

REPLICAS: Concord Library, Concord, Massachusetts; Memorial Hall, Harvard University, Cambridge, Massachusetts; Columbia University, New York; Whitney Museum of American Art, New York; Hall of Fame, New York University, New York.

REFERENCES: *Met. Mus. Bull.*, old series 2 (1907):87; *Catalogue of Sculpture* (Metropolitan Museum, 1908); M. F. Cresson, *Journey into Fame* (1947).

EXHIBITED: Exposition Universelle, Paris, 1889; Philadelphia Art Club, 1894; National Sculpture Society, New York, 1923.

GIFT OF DANIEL CHESTER FRENCH, 1907.

The Melvin Memorial   15.75

Also known as Mourning Victory. The original was designed as a memorial to Asa Heald Melvin, John Heald Melvin, and Samuel Melvin, three brothers who died in the Civil War. The monument was dedicated in 1909 in Sleepy Hollow Cemetery, Concord, Massachusetts. The copy in marble, cut by Piccirilli Brothers, was made especially for presentation to this Museum.

Marble, height 146 in. Signed: Daniel C. French. Dated 1915.

REPLICAS: Sleepy Hollow Cemetery, Concord, Massachusetts; Albright Art Gallery, Buffalo (plaster, presented by D. C. French in 1916).

REFERENCES: *Monumental News*, 18 (1909): 140; James C. Melvin, *The Melvin Memorial, Sleepy Hollow Cemetery* (1910); *Met. Mus. Bull.*, old series 10 (1915):78.

EXHIBITED: National Academy of Design, New York, *Winter Exhibition*, 1908 (plaster); National Sculpture Society, Buffalo (Albright Art Gallery), 1916 (plaster), and New York, 1923.

GIFT OF JAMES C. MELVIN, 1912.

Memory   19.47

Seated figure of a nude woman holding a mirror, cut by Piccirilli Brothers.

Marble, height 58 in. Signed: D. C. French, Sc. Dated 1919.

REFERENCES: R. Cortissoz, *New York Herald* (Feb. 9, 1919); *New York Herald* (Feb. 22, 1919); *Met. Mus. Bull.*, old series 14 (1919):46; M. O. Dewing, *American Magazine of Art*, 10 (1919):196; *Boston Evening Transcript* (Apr. 19, 1919).

EXHIBITED: Knoedler Galleries, New York, 1919; National Sculpture Society, New York, 1923; Baltimore Museum of Art, 1923.

GIFT OF HENRY WALTERS, 1919.

The Milmore Memorial   26.120

Also known as The Angel of Death and the Sculptor, this sculpture was designed in 1892 as a memorial to Martin Milmore (1844–1883). The original plaster was shown at the World's Columbian Exposition in Chicago in 1893, where it won wide popular acclaim. The bronze, erected in Forest Hills Cemetery, Boston, was cast in Paris and exhibited at the Salon in 1892, where it was awarded a medal of the third class. Milmore was a sculptor, credited by Lorado Taft with the somewhat dubious honor of having invented the typical

19.47

26.120

Civil War Soldier's and Sailor's Monument so widely copied by commercial manufacturers of "galvanized monuments."

Marble, height 92 in., width 99¾ in. Signed: D. C. French Sc. Dated 1926. Inscribed: The Milmore Memorial.

REPLICAS: Forest Hills Cemetery, Boston (bronze); Art Institute of Chicago (plaster); Corcoran Gallery of Art, Washington (plaster).

REFERENCES: *Met. Mus. Bull.*, old series 13 (1918):81; P. Remington, *Met. Mus. Bull.*, old series 21 (1926):162; L. Taft, *History of American Sculpture* (1930).

EXHIBITED: Paris, Salon of 1892 (bronze), Third Class Medal; World's Columbian Exposition, Chicago, 1893 (original plaster); Metropolitan Museum, 1918 (plaster).

GIFT OF A GROUP OF TRUSTEES, 1926.

Other Works

17.155.1. Medal commemorating the completion of the Catskill aqueduct. 1917. Bronze, diameter 3 in. 17.155.2, 17.156, 17.183. Three small duplicates. Bronze, silver, bronze, diameter 1½ in. Gift of Robert W. DeForest, 1917.

18.90. Medal commemorating the visit to New York of the French and British War Commission. Designed in collaboration with Evelyn B. Longman. 1917. Bronze, diameter 2¼ in. Gift of Cass Gilbert, 1918.

21.37. Medal commemorating the vision and achievement of the War Council, 1917–1919. Silver, diameter 2¾ in. 21.78. Duplicate. Gift of Robert W. DeForest, 1921.

Tablet in Armor Hall in memory of Bashford Dean. Designed by French. 1930. Bronze, 58 x 28¼ in.

57.147. Parian-ware group, illustrating Joe's Farewell, a scene from Charles Dickens's *Barnaby Rudge*. Designed by French. Height 9½ in. Gift of Mrs. Charles Beekman Bull, 1957, in memory of her mother, Alice Hawker Reimer.

John Talbott Donoghue
1853–1903

BORN in Chicago; died in Hamden, Connecticut. In 1875 Donoghue became a student at the Chicago Academy of Design and two years later won a scholarship for a year of study at the École des Beaux-Arts under Jouffroy. In 1880 he exhibited a plaster head, Phaedre, at the Paris Salon. After his return to the United States in 1881 his work attracted the attention of Oscar Wilde, who was lecturing in Chicago. The praise of so eminent a critic brought Donoghue a Chicago patron who enabled him to go to Paris again, where he studied for a time under Falguière. From 1884 to 1887 he was working in Rome, and he sent some of his works to Paris for exhibition in the Salons of 1884, 1886, and 1887. Returning to the United States, he made some portraits in Boston and there executed a full-length portrait statue of the boxer John L. Sullivan, then at the height of his fame. In the early nineties he was in Rome at work on his great masterpiece The Spirit Brooding over the Abyss, inspired by a line from Milton. This gigantic figure was intended for the World's Columbian Exposition in Chicago but because of the difficulties and expense of transportation never reached the Exposition. Part of it slowly fell to pieces on the Brooklyn docks; the rest was lost or destroyed in Rome. After this disaster Donoghue worked in New York as an architectural sculptor. He was commissioned to execute a figure of Saint Louis for the Appellate Court Building in New York and one of Saint Paul for the Library of Congress in Washington. His design for a McKinley Monument in Philadelphia was rejected. This blow to his pride eventually led to his suicide.

The Young Sophocles   27.65

This statue was first exhibited at the Salon in Paris in 1886 with the title The Young Sophocles Leading the Chorus of Victory after the Battle of Salamis, and was awarded Honorable

Mention. The plaster original (formerly in the Art Institute of Chicago) was made in Rome in 1885. Our example was cast in 1927 from a plaster acquired by the Museum in 1917, which was then given to the University of Nebraska. Nash stated that "of classical statues produced by Americans it is perhaps the most freshly inspired and pleasing."

Bronze, height 92½ in. Inscribed in Greek (on base): Sophocles Salamis. Founder's mark: Gorham Co.

REPLICAS: Art Institute of Chicago (bronze); University of Nebraska, Lincoln (plaster); collection of Mrs. Joy TenEyck, Baltimore (probably small; lent to Baltimore Museum of Art, *Inaugural Exhibition*, 1923).

REFERENCES: C. deKay, "The Young Sophokles," *Art Review* 1, no. 4 (1887); G. J. Zolnay, *The Art Department Illustrated* (Louisiana Purchase Exposition, 1904); "Donoghue's Young Sophocles," *Art World* (Jan. 1917); E. G. Nash, "Donoghue," *Dictionary of American Biography*.

EXHIBITED: Paris, Salon of 1886 (plaster), Honorable Mention; National Academy of Design, New York, *Annual Exhibition*, 1887; Royal Academy, London, 1890; World's Columbian Exposition, Chicago, 1893, First Prize; Louisiana Purchase Exposition, St. Louis, 1904; Pennsylvania Academy of the Fine Arts, Philadelphia, *Annual Exhibition*, 1906; Metropolitan Museum, 1918.

PURCHASE, ROGERS FUND, 1927.

27.65

Frederic Wellington Ruckstull

1853–1942

BORN in Breitenbach, France; died in New York. In 1855 Ruckstull was brought to the United States by his parents, who settled in St. Louis, Missouri. His persistent interest in modeling finally decided him, when he was thirty-two years old, to give up his position as manager of a toy-manufacturing firm. He set out for three years of study in Paris with funds supplied by a small group of St. Louis businessmen. Once in Paris he found he was too old to be admitted to the Académie des Beaux-Arts, but he studied at the Académie Julian and at the night classes in the Académie Colarossi. He studied drawing with Boulanger and Lefebvre and modeling under Tholenaar, Dampt, and Mercié. In his autobiography he says, "I could have become a private pupil of Rodin; but, as his works, all but a few, repelled me by their ugliness and brutal mannerisms, I preferred to be under the influence of the refined and poetic Mercié." In 1892 he opened a studio in New York.

Perhaps Ruckstull's most enduring monument is the National Sculpture Society, which was organized and nursed through its difficult initial stages largely by him alone (at least according to his own statements—Charles de-Kay also claimed to be the founder of the National Sculpture Society). The organization of the Society aroused much heated criticism, especially from sculptors not elected and from those who refused to join. Ruckstull's strong prejudices against anything modern in art exploded after the famous Armory Show in 1913 with a series of articles published in *The Art World*, a magazine that he established and edited and for which he wrote much of the text. This material was later published in a book, *Great Works of Art and What Makes Them Great* (1925). Ruckstull's views in these writings are very succinctly expressed, and he had no hesitation in calling his brother artists Bolshevists, lunatics, madmen, sadists, etc., in the most libelous and vituperative manner.

At the time of the first World War Ruckstull changed the spelling of his name from Ruckstuhl to Ruckstull.

Evening   20.125

In a letter to the Museum dated 1933 the sculptor described this work as follows: "I might say the statue expresses the *folding up toward evening*, after twilight, of all living things on the earth, . . . so I made my figure putting her arms around her head, . . . her face taking on an expression of drowsiness, short of sleep." In his book *Great Works of Art and What Makes Them Great* Ruckstull gives the following account: "In the summer of 1887 I began my first serious statue, *Evening*, and worked on it steadily for nine months, and sent it to the Salon of 1888, and then went on a seven weeks trip to Italy. I was then thirty five and undecided about continuing in sculpture. But, on my return, I found I had won an Honorable Mention . . . to my great astonishment and joy. This decided me to devote the balance of my life to art. I took the plaster statue to St. Louis, exhibited it at the annual 'exposition' held there and began a portrait bust of Mrs. Philipine Espenscheid Overstoltz. . . . When the portrait was finished

she was so pleased that she offered me the money to return to Paris and put my *Evening* into marble. . . . In 1889, [I] found a studio back of the Champs de Mars, and was soon at work carving in the marble my bust of Madame Overstolz and setting a marble cutter to work roughing out and 'pointing up' the marble copy of my plaster statue *Evening*, and when he had pointed up the figure, I began to finish the carving myself. . . . I worked steadily for fifteen months on the carving of my *Evening*, having decided to carve it myself in the marble, which is usually done for the sculptors, after they have modelled the statue in clay, and often by men more able as carvers, than are the sculptors who hire them. . . . I felt certain of winning a medal [at the Salon of 1891] on the marble *Evening*." The statue was deposited in this Museum in 1894 after the Chicago Exposition.

Marble, height 72 in. Signed: F. W. Ruckstuhl. Dated: Paris 1891. Inscribed: Le Soir.

REPLICAS: According to the sculptor the original plaster was destroyed, and no other copy was made.

REFERENCES: *New York World* (Dec. 30, 1894); *Catalogue of Sculpture* (Metropolitan Museum, 1908); F. W. Ruckstull, *Great Works of Art and What Makes Them Great* (1925).

EXHIBITED: Paris, Salon, 1888 (plaster), Honorable Mention, and 1891 (marble); Annual Exposition, St. Louis, 1889 (plaster); Society of American Artists, New York, 1893; World's Columbian Exposition, Chicago, 1893 (marble), Gold Medal.

PURCHASE, AMELIA B. LAZARUS FUND, 1920.

Henry Linder
1854–1910

BORN and died in Brooklyn, New York. After a brief apprenticeship with a marble-cutter Linder went to Munich, where he stud-

14.77

the date of his birth and said: "I think all other questions asked . . . as far as my individual self is concerned, are superficial, and pardon me if I do not answer any of them."

Medieval Art   14.77

A symbolic figure of a woman holding a chalice and a reliquary, probably a study for one of the figures representing the arts designed for the Fine Arts Building at the Louisiana Purchase Exposition, St. Louis, 1904.

Bronze, height 41 in. Signed: Henry Linder. Dated 1909.

EXHIBITED: National Sculpture Society, New York, *Linder Memorial Exhibition,* 1910.

PURCHASE, ROGERS FUND, 1914.

Louis Saint-Gaudens
1854–1913

BORN in New York; died in Cornish, New Hampshire. Louis Saint-Gaudens was the younger brother of Augustus Saint-Gaudens, by whom he was quite overshadowed. He was employed for many years as a studio assistant by his brother and did comparatively few works independently. He was awarded a silver medal at the Pan American Exposition in Buffalo in 1901 and was a member of the National Sculpture Society.

ied with Knabl. Later he spent a year in Rome. He returned to the United States in 1878 and earned his living by designing for silversmiths. He also designed hardware, andirons, and other decorative household equipment in metal. He developed an ornamental style that was doubtless the effect of his German training and was possibly influenced by the work of some British sculptors. His individual feeling for quaint decorative conceits made his work stand out from the general run of imitation French sculpture produced in this country by many of his contemporaries. Linder died in 1910 and was honored by a memorial exhibition held by the National Sculpture Society in that year. In 1902, when he was requested to send an autobiographical letter to the Museum, he replied by sending

Piping Pan   14.119

A garden figure, described as "a mischievous baby forest god." This example was possibly cast about 1900.

Bronze, height 43½ in. Signed: LSG (monogram). Founder's mark: Roman Bronze Works NY.

REPLICAS: Three examples were cast in bronze in 1914.

REFERENCE: R.M.J., *Met. Mus. Bull.,* old series 9 (1914):243.

EXHIBITED: Society of American Artists, New York, 1882 (as Young Pan); Pan American Exposition, Buffalo, 1901 (as Faun); Panama Pacific Exposition, San Francisco, 1915.

PURCHASE, ROGERS FUND, 1914.

Other Works

94.16.2. Congressional medal attributed to Saint-Gaudens. Inscribed: To Joseph Francis inventor and framer of the means for the life saving service of the country. 1888. Bronze, diameter 4 in. Gift of Isaac P. Francis through the Chamber of Commerce, 1894.

Charles Henry Niehaus

1855–1935

BORN in Cincinnati, Ohio; died in Cliffside, New Jersey. Niehaus practiced wood engraving and stonecutting in his youth. He began his art studies at the McMicken School of Design in Cincinnati and at twenty-two went to study at the Royal Academy in Munich, where he remained for four years. On his return to the United States in 1881 the State of Ohio and the City of Cincinnati both awarded him commissions for monuments to President Garfield. To execute these commissions he went to Rome, returning in 1886 to settle in New York. His work is characterized by a combination of heavy German realism faintly modified by neoclassic overtones, a mixture typical of the German academic tradition in which he was trained. In 1902 the sculptor sent to the Museum a seven-page document giving some autobiographical facts and a list of works executed and medals and honors won to that date. The greater number of Niehaus's works are large monuments, portrait statues, and architectural sculpture. No less than six portrait statues by Niehaus are in the Capitol in Washington. A booklet published in 1901 illustrates many of his monuments, some of which bear a strong resem-

blance to the work of other sculptors, notably his equestrian Sherman and his Admiral Farragut, which are very much like the statues by Saint-Gaudens. Taft said, "His collective works look as though they had come from a dozen different hands."

Caestus   07.50

The original of this figure of a boxer was made in Rome in 1883. In ancient times Greek and Roman boxers wore on their hands an arrangement of leather straps called a *caestus*. This was not padded like a modern boxing glove but was frequently weighted with lead or covered with iron knobs to increase the weight of the blow and the amount of the damage that could be inflicted, like its modern equivalent, the brass knuckle.

Bronze, height 38 in. Signed: C. H. Niehaus. Dated 1901. Founder's mark: Gorham Mfg. Co. Founders.

REPLICAS: According to the sculptor several replicas were cast in bronze, but none have been located.

REFERENCES: *Catalogue of Sculpture* (Metropolitan Museum, 1908); L. Taft, *History of American Sculpture* (1930).

EXHIBITED: National Academy of Design, New York, 1903; Louisiana Purchase Exposition, St. Louis, 1904; National Sculpture Society, Baltimore, 1908, Buffalo (Albright Art Gallery), 1916, and New York, 1923.

PURCHASE, ROGERS FUND, 1906.

Louis H. Sullivan

1856–1924

BORN in Boston; died in Chicago. Sullivan was trained as an architect at the Massachusetts Institute of Technology and at the École des Beaux-Arts in Paris. His great contribution to American art was the rediscovery of the basic aesthetic principle "form follows

92.91

that occupied most of the architects and architectural sculptors of his time. He wrote many articles on architecture and an autobiographical work, *The Autobiography of an Idea.* His principal pupil and follower was the architect and designer Frank Lloyd Wright.

A Design for a Bronze Door

92.91

Made for the Getty Tomb built by Sullivan in Graceland Cemetery, Chicago, in 1890. Of this structure La Follette said, "Modern architecture has yet to produce anything more beautiful in form and ornament than the Wainwright and Getty Tombs."

Plaster, height 88 in., width 42 in. Inscribed: Getty A.D. 1890.

REPLICAS: Getty Tomb, Graceland Cemetery, Chicago (bronze); Art Institute of Chicago (plaster).

REFERENCE: S. La Follette, *Art in America* (1929).

GIFT OF THE YALE AND TOWNE MANUFACTURING COMPANY, 1892.

function" and its application to architecture at a time when most American artists and architects were content with the debased academic standards of the French Second Empire. In the conception of this principle he was spiritually a follower of the American sculptor Horatio Greenough (see p. 1), who earlier had arrived at the same conclusion in his Stonecutter's Creed: "By beauty I mean the promise of function; By action I mean the presence of function; By character I mean the record of function."

Sullivan, not content with creating only the philosophical basis of modern architecture, also created an individual style of architectural ornament, based on the study of natural forms, as a protest against the copying of devitalized historical styles of ornament

Edward Clark Potter

1857–1923

BORN and died in New Haven, Connecticut. Potter was educated at Amherst College, and in 1888 and 1889 he studied animal sculpture under Mercié and Frémiet in Paris. Potter specialized in animal sculpture and made a particular study of the horse. In 1892 he worked with Daniel Chester French on the sculpture for the World's Columbian Exposition in Chicago. This began a life-long collaboration on many monuments, his part consisting in furnishing French with suitable steeds for his equestrian generals — among them Grant, Hooker, and Washington. Potter also made a number of monuments and statues independently of French, notably the Robert

Fulton in the Library of Congress, Washington, General Slocum in Gettysburg, Pennsylvania, and General Philip Kearny in Arlington Cemetery, Washington.

Sleeping Infant Faun Visited by an Inquisitive Rabbit   19.127

Made in 1919 from a plaster cast owned by the Museum.

Bronze, height 11 in. Signed: E. C. Potter. Founder's mark: Gorham Co. Founders.

REPLICA: Art Institute of Chicago (marble).

EXHIBITED: Metropolitan Museum, 1918.

PURCHASE, ROGERS FUND, 1919.

Francis Edwin Elwell

1858–1922

BORN in Concord, Massachusetts; died in Darien, Connecticut. Elwell was orphaned at the age of four and was brought up by his grandfather, Elisha Farrar, the village blacksmith, a minor Concord character and friend of Thoreau and Emerson. As a boy he worked in his grandfather's shop, where he learned to handle tools; as a young man he worked for Codman and Shurtleff, a firm of Boston instrument makers, where he is said to have "invented" some surgical instruments. His training in art began in Concord as a member of Miss May Alcott's drawing class. After some study in the Boston Museum's School Elwell was enabled to go to Paris in 1882, aided by loans from Miss Alcott and Daniel Chester French, who encouraged him in his determination to be a sculptor. In Paris he studied under Falguière and Jouffroy at the École des Beaux-Arts. He also studied at the Belgian Royal Academy at Ghent. In 1885 he opened a studio in New York and from 1903 to 1905 he was Curator of Ancient and Modern Statuary of this Museum. Besides carrying out the repair and "restoration" of the Roman sculpture in the Giustiniani Col-

lection, he also attempted to compile a biographical directory of American sculptors and wrote the first draft of a catalogue of the Museum's collection of modern sculpture (unpublished). Elwell's rather stormy temperament and his high opinion of himself as an artist led him into many difficulties. For several years he carried on a running fight with the officials of the National Sculpture Society, in the end becoming so agitated over this that he suffered a serious nervous breakdown, and the greater part of his remaining years were spent in retirement.

"Aqua Viva"   88.9

The title refers to the supposed street cry of the water vendors of Pompeii. This statue was first exhibited at the Paris Salon of 1885, where it was called "Aqua Viva" porteur d'eau de Pompeii. When it was shown the same year in New York, a criticism in *The Art Union* called it "an original figure, spirited and well worked out, with, however, more picturesqueness than grace."

Bronze, height 47½ in. Signed: F. E. Elwell. Dated 1884. Founder's mark: Cie des Bronzes Bruxelles cire perdue.

REFERENCES: *The Art Union*, 2 (1885):104; *Catalogue of Sculpture* (Metropolitan Museum, 1908).

EXHIBITED: Paris, Salon of 1885; American Art Galleries, New York, 1885; Royal Academy(?), London, 1885.

GIFT OF FRANCIS EDWIN ELWELL, 1888.

Herbert Adams

1858–1945

BORN in West Concord, Vermont; died in New York City. Adams studied at the Massachusetts Normal School of Art in Boston and then worked in Paris for five years (1885–1890) in the atelier of Mercié, where he came under the influence of the sculptors Rivière and Dampt. On his return to this country he rapidly became identified with leading academic artists and conservative art organizations, and he eventually became president of the National Academy of Design, president of the National Sculpture Society, a member of the National Commission on Fine Arts, and a trustee of the American Academy in Rome. His portraits of women were considered superb by other sculptors of his generation. In his *History of American Sculpture* Taft praised them without reserve, saying that they surpassed any work of modern sculpture, being unrivaled even in France. Adams's most popular work, the one that established his reputation, was a portrait bust of his wife (Adeline V. Pond, author of *The American Spirit in Sculpture*), awarded Honorable Mention at the Paris Salon of 1888 and exhibited in marble at the Salon of 1889. Among his larger works are several monumental statues (a form in which he was not overly adept) and bronze doors for the Library of Congress.

Adams received medals at the expositions in Chicago (1893), Charleston (1902), St. Louis (1904), and San Francisco (1915). In 1916 he was awarded the Watrous Gold Medal by the National Academy of Design, and in 1926 a gold medal by the American Academy of Arts and Letters.

La Jeunesse   11.14

This bust of a young girl was made about 1893 in the style of the French decorator and sculptor Louis Auguste Rivière (1857–1912).

Tinted marble and machine-carved fruitwood with decoration of paste jewels and twisted wire, height 22½ in. Signed: Herbert Adams.

REPLICAS: According to the sculptor five copies in terra cotta were made by Hall; three were destroyed, one was given to the family of Daniel Chester French; the other is now lost.

REFERENCES: *Met. Mus. Bull.*, old series 6 (1911):125 (quotation from Taft); L. Taft, *History of American Sculpture* (1930), p. 391 (description of this bust, erroneously called

11.14

The Rabbi's Daughter, the title of another work by Adams).

EXHIBITED: Society of American Artists, New York, 1894, no. 309 (plaster study); Pennsylvania Academy of the Fine Arts, Philadelphia, 1894; National Sculpture Society, New York, 1898 (ill., *The Craftsman*, 2[1898]:154); Pan American Exposition, Buffalo, 1901; Architectural League, New York, 1916.

PURCHASE, ROGERS FUND, 1911.

Singing Boys   32.62.2

This group portrait in low relief of the three sons of Fraser Campbell was cut by Piccirilli Brothers, New York.

White marble, height 36 in., width 44½ in. Inscribed: Evan, Arnold and William Fraser Campbell when they were ten eight and five years of age; (in scroll at left) Je suis prest Be mindful Fraser Campbell; (in wreath at right) Cornish NewHampshire Herbert Adams MDCCCXCIV.

REPLICA: According to the sculptor, the only replica was a small bronze plaque made for the Campbell family.

EXHIBITED: National Sculpture Society, Buffalo (Albright Art Gallery), 1916.

BEQUEST OF CHARLES W. GOULD, 1932.

Other Works

22.88. Memorial medal of Joseph H. Choate. 1922. Bronze, diameter 2½ in. Gift of Thomas T. Hoopes, 1922.

34.81.1. Medal dedicated to all fishermen. 1934. Bronze, diameter 2⅞ in. Gift of the Society of Medalists, 1934.

Adelaide Johnson

c. 1860–c. 1949

BORN in Plymouth, Illinois; died in Washington. Adelaide Johnson studied art at the St. Louis School of Design, where she was awarded a prize in 1877. In 1883 she was studying painting in Dresden and in 1884 was admitted to the studio of the sculptor Monteverde in Rome, where she worked for eleven years. Throughout her career she specialized in portraits of prominent women, among them Lucretia Mott, Elizabeth Cady Stanton, Susan B. Anthony, Mrs. H. O. P. Belmont, Emma Thursby, and Ella Wheeler Wilcox. Her monument to the founders of the women's rights movement in America is in the United States Capitol in Washington.

Susan B. Anthony   06.1264

This bust of the American pioneer in the feminist movement Susan B. Anthony (1820–1906) was modeled in her house in Rochester, New York, specially for display in the Court of Honor in the Women's Building at the World's Columbian Exposition in Chicago in 1893. It was reproduced as part of the monument to Lucretia Mott, Elizabeth Cady Stanton, and Susan B. Anthony erected in the Capitol in Washington and presented to Congress by the Women of the United States in 1921.

Marble, height 24 in. Dated 1892.

REPLICAS: Corcoran Gallery of Art, Washing-ton; collection of the sculptor, Washington (destroyed c. 1939).

REFERENCES: C. Clements, *Women in the Fine Arts* (1904), p. 380; *Catalogue of Sculpture* (Metropolitan Museum, 1908); "Sculptor of the New Woman," *The Sun* (New York?) (Apr. 4, 1909); C. Fairman, *Art and Artists of the Capitol* (1927).

EXHIBITED: World's Columbian Exposition, Chicago, 1893.

GIFT OF MRS. MURRAY WHITING FERRIS, 1906.

J. Stanley Connor

c. 1860–?

The only published record of Connor appears to be an article by C. Edwards Lester in a New York newspaper in 1883 at the time the bust of Cain was presented to the Museum. Although no birth date is given, information in the article seems to indicate that the sculptor was about twenty years old. "From his earliest years," Lester says, "he displayed the strongest proclivity for all forms of art and every facility was afforded him for its cultivation. At the age of eighteen his desire to visit Italy for study and observation under the best masters was gratified, and with an enthusiasm for work he soon began to develop an originality of conception and a facility of execution which amazed and delighted his teachers. So great was his progress during two years that he entered a studio of his own, where he surrounded himself with every appliance which ample means could suggest for his artistic improvement and the gratification of his ambition. . . . He clearly understood, in the beginning, what none but born artists ever know, that he must create and not borrow, he must work from within, and not from without—he must comprehend Nature in all her infinite and matchless moods . . . she must be worshipped as a lover, not dallied with as a mistress."

Cain   83.3

This bust is described by C. Edwards Lester as representing "the feelings of the first human murderer as he became fully conscious of his terrible crime. . . . If artist ever sculptured the worm that never dies, young Stanley Connor did it in the bust of Cain." The bust was presented to the Museum by the sculptor's mother.

Marble, height 26 in. Signed: J. Stanley Connor. Inscribed (on back): Cain.

GIFT OF MRS. JOHN ANDERSON, 1883.

Edwin Willard Deming

1860–1942

BORN in Ashland, Ohio; died in New York. As a boy Deming lived on the prairie frontier in Illinois, where he became well acquainted with the ways of the Indians, his friends and later the subjects of his paintings. As an artist he was largely self-taught. In 1883 he spent a winter in New York studying at the Art Students League, and the following year he studied in Paris at the Académie Julian under the painters Lefebvre and Boulanger. He returned to the United States in 1885 and spent much of his time thereafter among the Indian tribes of the Far West. Some of his mural paintings of Indian life are in the American Museum of Natural History, New York. His work as a sculptor is limited to a few small bronze studies of wild animals and Indians, most of them done between 1905 and 1910.

The Fight   07.42

Statuette of a grizzly bear attacked by a panther, made about 1906.

Bronze, height 7¾ in. Signed: E. W. Deming. Copyrighted; founder's mark: Roman Bronze Works.

REPLICAS: Gibbes Memorial Art Gallery, Charleston, South Carolina; Brookgreen Gardens, South Carolina; private collection, New York (formerly in collection of Theodore Roosevelt).

REFERENCES: L. Taft, *History of American Sculpture* (1930), p. 567; *The Spur*, 65 (1940): 19; B. G. Proske, *Brookgreen Gardens, Sculpture* (1943).

EXHIBITED: Architectural League, New York, 1907; Pennsylvania Academy of the Fine Arts, Philadelphia, 1909; Alaska-Yukon Pacific Exposition, Seattle, 1909; National Sculpture Society, Buffalo (Albright Art Gallery), 1916; 460 Park Avenue Gallery, New York, 1940.

PURCHASE, ROGERS FUND, 1907.

Mutual Surprise   08.69

A grizzly bear cub confronted by a turtle.

Bronze, height 9½ in. Signed: E. W. Deming. Dated 1907. Copyrighted; founder's mark: Roman Bronze Works N.Y.

REPLICAS: About five replicas are believed to have been cast in bronze.

EXHIBITED: Architectural League, New York, 1906, 1908; Pennsylvania Academy of the Fine Arts, Philadelphia, 1909; Alaska-Yukon Pacific Exposition, Seattle, 1909; Albright Art Gallery, Buffalo, 1912; 460 Park Avenue Gallery, New York, 1940.

PURCHASE, ROGERS FUND, 1908.

Frederic Remington

1861–1909

BORN in Canton, New York; died in Ridgefield, Connecticut. In a letter written to the Museum in 1902 Remington says that he was largely self-taught, having studied only one year at the Yale Art School. He mentions "hundreds of illustrations and numerous paintings" (the Museum has one painting by Remington, Cavalry Charge on the Southern Plains) and the following books: *Pony Tracks*, *Crooked Trails*, *Sundown Leflare*, *Men with the Bark On*, and *The Way of the Indian*. He lists some pieces of sculpture and notes the number of copies made of each: The Bronco Buster, statuette, unlimited; The Wounded Bunkie, fourteen copies; The Norther, one copy in Cleveland, three owned by Schley, one owned by Colby of Grange; The Buffalo Signal, one "lost wax" owned by French Devereau of Cleveland; The Cheyenne, unlimited.

Remington's only monumental bronze sculpture is The Cowboy in Fairmount Park, Philadelphia. He evidently considered himself first an illustrator and writer. His attitude toward his sculpture is suggested in another letter (1895): "When you Europeans get your eyes on my bronze [Bronco Buster] you will say: 'Ah! there! America has got a winner.' It's the biggest thing I ever did, and if some of these rich sinners over here will cough up and buy a couple of dozen, I will go into the mud business." That his bronzes were considered more illustrative than sculptural is borne out by Taft's comment: "[He] has also

been tempted to carry certain of his illustrations over into another medium, and it must be confessed that, while they remain illustrations, this clever artist seems as much at home in one form of expression as in the other. Mr. Remington is not an interpreter, nor is he ever likely to conceive a theme sculpturally; but his dashing compositions not only picture with much skill the machinery and paraphernalia of four-footed locomotion, but occasionally suggest somewhat of the spirit of the centaur life of the West."

The Bronco Buster   07.78

Remington's first attempt at modeling, made in New Rochelle, New York. This example was purchased directly from the artist.

Bronze, height 23 in. Inscribed: Copyright by Frederic Remington. Founder's mark: Roman Bronze Works, N.Y. Tiffany & Co., (serial number under base) No. 61.

REPLICAS: Brookgreen Gardens, South Carolina; Amherst College, Amherst, Massachusetts; Remington Memorial, Ogdensburg, New York; Philbrook Art Museum, Tulsa, Oklahoma. According to published records between two hundred and two hundred and forty bronze replicas in this size were made during Remington's lifetime. (For large-size replicas see The Bronco Buster, following.)

REFERENCES: A. Hoeber, "From Ink to Clay," *Harper's Weekly* (Oct. 19, 1895); *Catalogue of Sculpture* (Metropolitan Museum, 1908); P. Bigelow, *New York State Historical Association Quarterly Journal*, 10 (1929):48; B. G. Proske, *Brookgreen Gardens, Sculpture* (1943); H. McCracken, *Frederic Remington* (1947).

EXHIBITED: National Sculpture Society, New York, 1898; Pan American Exposition, Buffalo, 1901; Pennsylvania Academy of the Fine Arts, Philadelphia, 1910; Panama Pacific Exposition, San Francisco, 1915; Baltimore Museum of Art, 1923; Museum of Modern Art, New York, 1932–1933; New-York Historical Society, New York, 1947.

PURCHASE, ROGERS FUND, 1907.

07.78

The Bronco Buster 39.65.45

The same subject as the preceding entry but larger.

Bronze, height 32¼ in. Inscribed: Presented to Jacob Ruppert Jr. by the Lager Beer Brewers Board of Trade of New York and Vicinity Nov. 9th 1910 Copyright by Frederic Remington. Founder's mark: Roman Bronze Works, N.Y. No. 2.

REPLICAS: Remington Memorial, Ogdensburg, New York. About five bronzes are believed to have been cast in the large size.

REFERENCES: P. Remington, "The Bequest of Jacob Ruppert," *Met. Mus. Bull.*, old series 34 (1939):169; see preceding entry.

EXHIBITED: See preceding entry.

BEQUEST OF JACOB RUPPERT, 1939.

The Wounded Bunkie 39.65.46

Two soldiers on running horses. One soldier partly supports his wounded companion (bunkie: bunk mate). This is Remington's second attempt at modeling.

Bronze, height 21¾ in. Inscribed: Copyright by Frederic Remington 1896. Founder's mark: Cast by the Henry Bonnard Bronze Co N Y 1896.

REPLICAS: According to Remington fourteen examples of this subject were cast in bronze.

REFERENCES: P. Remington, "The Bequest of Jacob Ruppert," *Met. Mus. Bull.*, old series 34 (1939):169; H. McCracken, *Frederic Remington* (1947).

EXHIBITED: National Sculpture Society, New York, 1898; Pan American Exposition, Buffalo, 1901.

BEQUEST OF JACOB RUPPERT, 1939.

The Wicked Pony 39.65.48

A bucking bronco, his rider thrown to the ground beside him; also called The Fallen Rider. The original plaster is believed to have

39.65.46

39.65.48

been destroyed by fire at the Henry-Bonnard Foundry in 1898.

Bronze, height 21⅞ in. Signed (twice): Frederic Remington. Copyrighted (1898); founder's mark: The Henry Bonnard Bronze Co. Founders N Y 1896.

REPLICAS: Between five and ten examples of this subject were probably cast in bronze.

REFERENCES: P. Remington, "The Bequest of Jacob Ruppert," *Met. Mus. Bull.*, old series 34 (1939):169; H. McCracken, *Frederic Remington* (1947).

BEQUEST OF JACOB RUPPERT, 1939.

The Scalp   39.65.49

An Indian on a pony, holding aloft a scalp lock, made about 1898.

Bronze, height 22¾ in. Inscribed: Copyright by Frederic Remington. Founder's mark: Roman Bronze Works N Y, No 7.

39.65.49

REPLICAS: About twenty-five examples of this subject are believed to have been cast in bronze.

REFERENCES: P. Remington, "The Bequest of Jacob Ruppert," *Met. Mus. Bull.*, old series 34 (1939):169; H. McCracken, *Frederic Remington* (1947).

BEQUEST OF JACOB RUPPERT, 1939.

The Cheyenne   07.80

An Indian on a pony. This example was purchased directly from the artist.

Bronze, height 22½ in. Inscribed: Copyright 1901 by Frederic Remington. Founder's mark: Tiffany & Co., No. 19.

REPLICAS: About fifty bronze casts probably were made during Remington's lifetime.

REFERENCES: *Catalogue of Sculpture* (Metropolitan Museum, 1908); H. McCracken, *Frederic Remington* (1947).

EXHIBITED: Panama Pacific Exposition, San Francisco, 1915.

PURCHASE, ROGERS FUND, 1907.

Comin' through the Rye   39.65.44

This group of four cowboys on ponies running abreast, made about 1902, is sometimes called Off the Range. A life-size replica in plaster stood at the entrance to The Pike, the amusement area of the Louisiana Purchase Exposition in St. Louis in 1904, with the title Cowboys Shooting Up a Western Town. The same group in plaster was exhibited on the grounds of the Lewis and Clark Exposition in Portland, Oregon, in 1905.

Bronze, height 27¼ in. Inscribed: Copyrited Frederic Remington. Founder's mark: Roman Bronze Works N Y.

REPLICAS: Estimates on the number of examples of this subject cast in bronze vary between six and fifteen.

07.80

39.65.44

REFERENCES: *Official Guide* (Louisiana Purchase Exposition, 1904); P. Remington, "The Bequest of Jacob Ruppert," *Met. Mus. Bull.*, old series 34 (1939):169; H. McCracken, *Frederic Remington* (1947).

EXHIBITED: Louisiana Purchase Exposition, St. Louis, 1904.

BEQUEST OF JACOB RUPPERT, 1939.

The Mountain Man   07.79

A man riding a horse down a very steep incline, sometimes called The Trapper, or The Mountain Trapper. This example, made about 1903, was purchased directly from the artist.

Bronze, height 28 in. Signed: Frederic Remington. Copyrighted; founder's mark: Roman Bronze Works Tiffany & Co, No. 9.

REPLICAS: About forty replicas are believed to have been cast in bronze.

REFERENCES: *Catalogue of Sculpture* (Metropolitan Museum, 1908); H. McCracken, *Frederic Remington* (1947).

EXHIBITED: Pennsylvania Academy of the Fine Arts, Philadelphia, 1910.

PURCHASE, ROGERS FUND, 1907.

A Sergeant   39.65.52

A bust, also called A Rough Rider Sergeant, made about 1904.

Bronze, height 11¼ in. Signed: Frederic Remington. Copyrighted; founder's mark: Roman Bronze Works N Y.

REPLICAS: The number of examples of this subject cast in bronze is estimated variously from fifty to more than a hundred.

REFERENCES: P. Remington, "The Bequest of Jacob Ruppert," *Met. Mus. Bull.*, old series 34 (1939):169; H. McCracken, *Frederic Remington* (1947).

BEQUEST OF JACOB RUPPERT, 1939.

Dragoons—1850   07.77

Two soldiers and two Indians on horseback in running fight. This example, made in 1905, was purchased directly from the artist.

Bronze, height 28 in. Signed: Frederic Remington. Copyrighted; founder's mark: Roman Bronze Works N.Y.

REPLICAS: Between three and seven bronze replicas probably were cast.

REFERENCES: *Catalogue of Sculpture* (Metropolitan Museum, 1908); H. McCracken, *Frederic Remington* (1947).

PURCHASE, ROGERS FUND, 1907.

The Rattlesnake   39.65.43

A cowboy on a pony shying at a rattlesnake at its hoofs. This sculpture, sometimes called The Snake in the Path, was made about 1905.

Bronze, height 23¼ in. Signed: Frederic Remington. Copyrighted; founder's mark: Roman Bronze Works N.Y.

REPLICAS: Between eighty and a hundred bronze casts of this subject probably were made.

REFERENCES: P. Remington, "The Bequest of Jacob Ruppert," *Met. Mus. Bull.*, old series 34 (1939):169; H. McCracken, *Frederic Remington* (1947).

EXHIBITED: Panama Pacific Exposition, San Francisco, 1915.

BEQUEST OF JACOB RUPPERT, 1939.

39.65.43

The Outlaw   39.65.50

A cowboy on a bucking bronco, made about 1906.

Bronze, height 22½ in. Signed: Frederic Remington. Copyrighted; founder's mark: Roman Bronze Works N Y, No. 18.

REPLICAS: The number of examples of this subject cast in bronze has been estimated variously between twenty-five and a hundred.

REFERENCES: P. Remington, "The Bequest of Jacob Ruppert," *Met. Mus. Bull.*, old series 34 (1939):169; H. McCracken, *Frederic Remington* (1947).

39.65.50

EXHIBITED: Pennsylvania Academy of the Fine Arts, Philadelphia, 1910; Cincinnati Art Museum, 1910.

BEQUEST OF JACOB RUPPERT, 1939.

The Savage 39.65.51

Also called Head of an Indian Brave.

Bronze, height 11 in. Signed: Frederic Remington. Dated 1908. Copyrighted; founder's mark: Roman Bronze Works N Y, No. 10.

REPLICAS: About twenty examples of this subject are believed to have been cast in bronze.

REFERENCES: P. Remington, "The Bequest of Jacob Ruppert," *Met. Mus. Bull.*, old series 34 (1939):169; H. McCracken, *Frederic Remington* (1947).

BEQUEST OF JACOB RUPPERT, 1939.

Trooper of the Plains—1868
39.65.47

A statuette of a soldier on a galloping horse, made about 1909.

39.65.47

Bronze, height 24⅞ in. Inscribed: Copyright Frederic Remington. Founder's mark: Roman Bronze Works N Y, No. 5.

REPLICAS: About ten examples of this subject are believed to have been cast in bronze.

REFERENCES: P. Remington, "The Bequest of Jacob Ruppert," *Met. Mus. Bull.*, old series 34 (1939):169; H. McCracken, *Frederic Remington* (1947).

EXHIBITED: Pennsylvania Academy of the Fine Arts, Philadelphia, 1910; Cincinnati Art Museum, 1910.

BEQUEST OF JACOB RUPPERT, 1939.

William Ordway Partridge
1861–1930

BORN in Paris; died in New York. Partridge's father was foreign agent for the New York merchant A. T. Stewart. Partridge was educated in New York at Columbia College, and as a young man he appeared on the stage for a year as a member of Wallack's Theatre Company in a production of *David Copperfield*. He was trained as a sculptor in Rome under Pio Welenski and in Florence under Galli. He also studied in Berlin and Paris. A number of his monumental works are to be found in New York City, notably a Pietà in St. Patrick's Cathedral, a statue of Samuel J. Tilden on Riverside Drive, and in Brooklyn statues of General Grant and Alexander Hamilton. He also designed the Joseph Pulitzer tomb in Woodlawn Cemetery, a statue of Pocahontas in Jamestown, Virginia, a Shakespeare in Chicago, and a colossal Satyr for the Newport Golf and Pleasure Club, as well as many portrait busts of prominent men. He lectured on art at the Concord School of Philosophy and Leland Stanford University and was a professor at George Washington University in Washington. He was also the author of several books of poetry, notably *The Song Life of a*

22.59

Sculptor (1895), and a number of magazine articles on American sculpture and sculptors. The last few years of his life were spent in illness, and his death may have been hastened by the discovery that all of his plaster casts, stored in the basement of a New York apartment house, had been destroyed by having tons of coal dumped over them.

Peace   22.59

Head of a woman, made about 1899.

Marble, height 15½ in.

REPLICAS: Four variants, some in bronze, are said to have been made.

REFERENCE: *The Works and Sculpture of William Ordway Partridge* (1914).

EXHIBITED: Pennsylvania Academy of the Fine Arts, Philadelphia, 1899; Metropolitan Museum, 1918.

PURCHASE, ROGERS FUND, 1922.

Arthur B. Davies

1862–1928

BORN in Utica, New York; died in Italy. Davies' artistic talents showed themselves when he was still a boy, and his parents encouraged his early efforts as a painter. In 1878 his family moved to Chicago, where he studied at the Academy of Design. In 1880 he went to Mexico for two years and worked there as an engineering draftsman. On his return to Chicago he studied at the Chicago Art Institute. He went to New York in 1886 to study at the Art Students League, and in 1893 Benjamin Altman made it possible for him to go to Italy.

Davies' principal fame rests on his work as a painter and an early patron of modern art in America: he was one of the principal organizers of the famous Armory Show in 1913. In addition to producing designs for tapestries, rugs, and textiles he worked as a lithographer, etcher, wood-carver, and sculptor. A memorial exhibition of his work was held at The Metropolitan Museum of Art in 1930.

Nude   55.150

A bas-relief.

Bronze, height 7½ in.

GIFT OF FREDERIC NEWLIN PRICE, 1955.

Charles Grafly

1862–1929

BORN and died in Philadelphia. At the age of seventeen Grafly was an apprentice in carving at Struthers' Stoneyard. He studied in Philadelphia at the Spring Garden Institute and at the Pennsylvania Academy of the Fine Arts. In 1888 he went to Paris to study at the École des Beaux-Arts and at the Académie Julian, where he remained for four years. He exhibited in the Salon of 1890. Upon his return to Philadelphia in 1892, he began teaching at the Drexel Institute of Technology and at the Pennsylvania Academy of the Fine Arts.

Grafly's most important work is the memorial to General George Gordon Meade in Washington. This is a group led by a symbolic figure of war and seven other symbolic figures escorting General Meade. He is also noted for his portrait busts of artists, which won him numerous awards. He was awarded medals by the Pennsylvania Academy of the Fine Arts and at the expositions in Paris, Buffalo, Charleston, and Buenos Aires. He was a member of the National Sculpture Society, the Architectural League of New York, and the National Institute of Arts and Letters.

Morris Gray   53.108

Morris Gray (1856–1931) was the fifth president of the Museum of Fine Arts in Boston.

Bronze, height 26½ in. Signed: Charles Grafly. Dated Aug. 1923. Inscribed (on back): Morris Gray fifth president of the Museum of Fine Arts Boston 1856–. Founder's mark: Roman Bronze Works N.Y.

GIFT OF MRS. CORTLANDT PARKER, 1953.

Isadore Konti

1862–1938

BORN in Vienna; died in Yonkers, New York. Konti worked as a studio assistant with Karl Bitter when he first came to the United States. For many years he had a studio in Yonkers, New York. In 1902 Konti sent the following letter to the Museum:

"I was born . . . in Vienna, and studied there in the Imperial Academy with Edmund Hellmer and Karl Kundmann. I then went to Italy on a scholarship for two years. I have received neither medals nor distinction. I came to this country in 1892, and worked on the sculpture for the World's Fair in Chicago.

I then settled here in New York, and made many decorative works for private and public buildings. Among the works I did in Vienna are, the bust of the Emperor Francis Joseph . . . in 1886; a monument to the Poet, Count Auersperg . . . in 1882; and the monument to Turnvater Jahn . . . in 1887.

"Among my most prominent works in this country are, a relief on the door of Grace Chapel, New York in 1894; two spandrels on the Home Life Insurance Company's building, New York in 1894; the interior work in the residence of Elbridge T. Gerry, New York, in 1896; The Stewart Rhinelander Memorial, a baptismal font in Holy Trinity Church . . . 1898; the group of 'The West Indies' and the spandrels 'The North and East Rivers' for the Dewey Arch, in 1899; the group Pan and Cupid in a private collection, in 1899; an ideal figure, 'Inspiration' in 1900. Sculpture for the Pan American Exposition at Buffalo, 1891 . . . and a memorial tablet . . . in Syracuse in 1902."

George Fiske Comfort   31.52

Bust of George Fiske Comfort (1833–1910), American educator, who was one of the founders of the Metropolitan Museum and a member of the Executive Committee of its Board of Trustees in 1870 and 1871. The statement of the aims and purposes of the Museum as set forth in its charter is based upon his ideas if not couched in his words. His conception of art museums as educational institutions, embodied in his address to the Incorporators of the Metropolitan Museum of Art in 1869, set the direction in which all American art museums have developed. Professor Comfort left New York City in 1872 to become founder and dean of the College of Art at Syracuse University, New York.

Plaster, height 26½ in. Signed: I. Konti. Dated 1902. Inscribed: George F. Comfort.

REFERENCES: Winifred E. Howe, *A History of the Metropolitan Museum of Art* (1913), and *George Fiske Comfort, One of the Founders of the Metropolitan Museum of Art* (1934).

EXHIBITED: National Sculpture Society, Madison Square Garden, New York, 1903.

EX COLL. Ralph M. Comfort, New York.

PURCHASE, TRUSTEES' CONTRIBUTION, 1931.

The Genius of Immortality   16.27

Seated figure of a nude man, made about 1912.

Bronze, height 25¼ in. Signed: I. Konti. Founder's mark: Roman Bronze Works N.Y.

REPLICAS: Detroit Institute of Arts. According to the sculptor other replicas were made and sold by Gorham Co.; one was purchased by the Italian government.

EXHIBITED: Cincinnati Art Museum, 1911; Architectural League, New York, 1912; Panama Pacific Exposition, San Francisco, 1915 (as Immortality of Genius in cat.); National Sculpture Society, Buffalo (Albright Art Gallery), 1916.

PURCHASE, ROGERS FUND, 1916.

Other Works

06.193. Medal commemorating the two-hundred-and-fiftieth anniversary of Jewish settlement in the United States. 1905. Bronze, diameter 3 in. 11.99. Duplicate. Gift of Isadore Konti, 1906 and 1911.

Albert Pike Lucas

1862–1945

BORN in Jersey City, New Jersey; died in New York. Lucas studied painting in Paris under Hébert at the École des Beaux-Arts and later with Boulanger, Dagnan-Bouveret, and Courtois; he was much better known as a painter than as a sculptor. He lived in France from 1882 to 1904 and traveled extensively in Europe. After returning to the United States, Lucas was president of the Allied Artists of America and a member of many other art organizations, notably the National Sculpture Society, the National Arts Club, and the Salmagundi Club. In 1927 he was elected a National Academician.

Ecstase   29.108

Head of a young girl, made before 1914.

Marble, height 20 in. Signed: Albert P. Lucas.

GIFT OF ALBERT PIKE LUCAS, 1929.

Alexander Phimister Proctor

1862–1950

BORN in Bosanquit, Ontario, Canada; died in Palo Alto, California. Proctor spent the early part of his life in Denver, Colorado, where he made sketches of wild animals in the Rocky Mountains. He began his formal art training in New York at the National Academy of Design and the Art Students League. After a period of study in Paris with Puech and Injalbert, he returned to New York, where he was employed by other sculptors, especially Saint-Gaudens. In 1895 he received the first Rinehart Scholarship for five years of study in Paris, where he worked at the Académie Julian and the Académie Colarossi. After his return to the United States, he traveled widely and lived in various places, mostly in the western states.

Proctor received awards at the Louisiana Purchase Exposition in St. Louis in 1904 and the Panama Pacific Exposition in San Francisco in 1915, and from the Architectural League in 1911. He was a member of the National Sculpture Society, the National Academy of Design, and the National Institute of Arts and Letters. Some of his most familiar works are the pair of couchant tigers at Nassau Hall, Princeton University, and the charging bison on the Q Street Bridge in Washington.

Fawn
12.53

Bronze, height 6¾ in. Signed: A. P. Proctor. Dated 1893. Copyrighted.

EXHIBITED: Art Institute of Chicago, 1898; Pennsylvania Academy of the Fine Arts, Philadelphia, 1899; Exposition Universelle, Paris, 1900, Gold Medal; Pan American Exposition, Buffalo, 1901.

PURCHASE, ROGERS FUND, 1912.

Buffalo
39.65.55

Originally designed to ornament the pylons of the Q Street Bridge, Washington.

Bronze, height 13¼ in. Signed: A. Phimister Proctor. Dated 1912. Inscribed: Model of Buffalo for Q Street Bridge, Washington D.C. Copyrighted; founder's mark: Gorham Co. Founders OPF.

REPLICAS: Metropolitan Museum (bronze; see following entry); Q Street Bridge, Washington.

REFERENCE: P. Remington, *Met. Mus. Bull.*, old series 34 (1939):172.

EXHIBITED: Cincinnati Art Museum, 1912; Art Institute of Chicago, 1912; National Academy of Design, New York, *Winter Exhibition*, 1912, 1913; Albright Art Gallery, Buffalo, 1913; Panama Pacific Exposition, San Francisco, 1915. (Earlier studies of buffaloes by Proctor, which may be identical or similar to the above, were exhibited: National Sculpture Society, New York, 1898; Architectural League, New York, 1899; Pan American Exposition, Buffalo, 1901; Pennsylvania Academy of the Fine Arts, Philadelphia, 1904, 1910; Albright Art Gallery, Buffalo, 1909.)

BEQUEST OF JACOB RUPPERT, 1939.

Buffalo
48.149.29

Duplicate of the preceding entry.

BEQUEST OF GEORGE DUPONT PRATT, 1935.

Morgan Stallion
39.65.61

This statue of a horse was made about 1913.

Bronze, height 15½ in. Signed: A. Phimister Proctor. Founder's mark: Gorham Co. Founders ORO.

REPLICAS: About ten replicas are believed to have been cast in bronze.

REFERENCE: P. Remington, *Met. Mus. Bull.*, old series 34 (1939):172.

EXHIBITED: Proctor exhibited statuettes called American Horse, Horse, Stallion, all or none of which may be identical with the Morgan Stallion. Pan American Exposition, Buffalo, 1901 (as American Horse); Louisiana Purchase Exposition, St. Louis, 1904 (as Stallion); Pennsylvania Academy of the Fine Arts, Philadelphia, 1904; Panama Pacific Exposition, San Francisco, 1915 (as American Horse); National Sculpture Society, Buffalo (Albright Art Gallery), 1916 (as Horse).

BEQUEST OF JACOB RUPPERT, 1939.

48.149.26

The Buckaroo   48.149.26

A cowboy on a bucking pony.

Bronze, height 28½ in. Signed: A. P. Proctor. Dated 1915. Inscribed: (on front of base) The Buckaroo; (on side of base) Cast for Geo. D. Pratt by A. P. P. Copyrighted; founder's mark: Roman Bronze Works N.Y.

REPLICA: Civic Center, Denver.

EXHIBITED: Olympic Fine Arts Exhibition, Amsterdam, Holland, 1928.

BEQUEST OF GEORGE DUPONT PRATT, 1935.

27.21.8

Frederick William MacMonnies

1863–1937

BORN in Brooklyn, New York; died in New York. MacMonnies' artistic talents were supposedly inherited from his mother, who was a relative of the painter Benjamin West. In 1880 he was employed as a studio assistant by Augustus Saint-Gaudens and began to study in the evening classes of the National Academy of Design and at the Art Students League. In 1884 he went to Paris, where he studied with Falguière and Mercié. In 1887 he returned to work with Saint-Gaudens in New York, remaining until 1889, when again he went to Paris. He did not return until the beginning of the first World War, and this long residence in France, with his earlier training there, gave his work such a strong French flavor that it is almost indistinguishable from contemporary French sculpture. In 1891 he was awarded a Medal of the Second Class at the Salon, an honor never before conferred upon an American sculptor.

MacMonnies' fame was established in this country by his Columbian Fountain at the Exposition in Chicago in 1893—an ornate barge full of allegorical ladies struggling with improbable oars, inspired by a similar construction at the Paris Exposition of 1889. This fountain was called the finest sculpture on the exposition grounds. Many of his later works were received with somewhat less acclaim. His Bacchante, presented to the Boston Public Library in 1897, aroused a storm of protest engineered in large part by the Women's Christian Temperance Union. The ladies were not overly shocked by the nudity of the Bacchante, but her tipsiness and the fact that she held an infant in her arms seemed to them an outrageous insult to pure American motherhood. His Venus and Adonis had to be withdrawn from an outdoor exhibition in New Rochelle, and his Civic Virtue, made for the City Hall Plaza in New York, aroused so much criticism and protest that it was removed to a less conspicuous site in Brooklyn. His Nathan Hale in City Hall Park, however, appeared to please everyone and to be a model public monument. In his later years he was greatly influenced by Rodin. Many of MacMonnies' works are to be found in Brooklyn, where his principal patron, James Stranahan, lived. He received many medals and honors. He won the Grand Prize at the Paris Exposition in 1900; he was a member of the National Institute of Arts and Letters and was a Chevalier of the Legion of Honor. His wife Mary Fairchild MacMonnies was a painter of murals. His best-known pupil was the designer of fountains, Janet Scudder.

The Museum has one drawing by MacMonnies, a charcoal called The Old Cobbler, and a portrait in oil of May Palmer.

Diana   27.21.9

One of MacMonnies' earliest works, modeled in 1889, his first Salon success. In style it is indistinguishable from the works of his teacher Falguière.

Bronze, height 30¾ in. Signed: F. MacMonnies. Dated: Paris 1890. Inscribed: Esq. [esquisse: sketch] To My Friend Edward D. Adams. Founder's Mark: Gruet Fondeur Paris.

REFERENCES: Paris, Salon of 1889, cat.; L. Taft, *History of American Sculpture* (1930).

EXHIBITED: Paris, Salon of 1889 (plaster), Honorable Mention; Architectural League, New York, 1891 (lent by Stanford White); Society of American Artists, New York, 1891 (lent by Edward D. Adams); Philadelphia Art Club, 1895; Albright Art Gallery, Buffalo, 1909, and 1916 (National Sculpture Society).

GIFT OF EDWARD D. ADAMS, 1927.

Young Faun and Heron   27.21.8

A fountain group, designed to be placed in a niche, made about 1890.

Bronze, height 27¾ in. Signed: F. MacMonnies. Founder's mark: Gruet Fondeur Paris. A first proof.

REPLICA: Cleveland Museum of Art.

REFERENCE: Paris, Salon of 1890, cat.

EXHIBITED: Paris, Salon of 1890; Society of American Artists, New York, 1891 (lent by Edward Adams); Philadelphia Art Club, 1895; Cincinnati Art Museum, 1900 (lent by Theodore B. Starr, Inc.); Fine Arts Building, New York, *Retrospective of American Art*, 1921.

GIFT OF EDWARD D. ADAMS, 1927.

97.19

Bacchante and Infant Faun   97.19

This bronze was offered as a gift to the Boston Public Library by the architect Charles Follen McKim in 1896 for placement in the Library's garden court. After a great storm of public protest stirred up by the Women's Christian Temperance Union against its "drunken indecency," the gift was rejected by the Library. McKim then presented the bronze to this Museum.

Bronze, height 83 in. Signed: F. MacMonnies. Dated 1893. Founder's mark: Thiébaut Frères Fondeurs Paris.

REPLICAS: Whitney Museum of American Art, New York (small bronze); Musée du Luxembourg, Paris; Boston Museum of Fine Arts; Cleveland Museum of Art. Plaster replicas were still being sold by a Boston plaster firm in 1928. A small bronze replica formerly decorated the newel post of the main stairway of Richard Canfield's New York gambling house.

REFERENCES: *Catalogue of Sculpture* (Metropolitan Museum, 1908); J. W. McSpadden, *Famous Sculptors of America* (1927); Charles Moore, *The Life and Times of Charles Follen McKim* (1929).

EXHIBITED: Paris, Salon of 1894 (bronze); Architectural League, New York, 1895 (small bronze, priced $250); Exposition Universelle, Paris, 1900; Cincinnati Museum of Art, 1900 (lent by Theodore B. Starr, Inc.); Albright Art Gallery, Buffalo, 1909; Fine Arts Building, New York, *Retrospective of American Art*, 1921; Baltimore Museum of Art, 1923.

GIFT OF CHARLES FOLLEN MCKIM, 1897.

Boy and Duck   22.61

A fountain group sometimes called Duck Baby. A replica was presented to the City of Brooklyn and erected in Prospect Park in 1896. Lorado Taft mentioned it in a review of the National Sculpture Society's Exhibition of 1898, saying, "This fountain was a tiny gem from MacMonnies' Parisian studio, a regular

22.61

Verrocchio baby holding aloft a struggling duck."

Bronze, height 46 in. including marble and bronze base. Copyrighted.

REPLICA: Prospect Park, Brooklyn, New York.

REFERENCES: L. Taft, "National Sculpture Society Exhibition 1898" (review), *The Craftsman*, 2 (1898):124; *Catalogue of Works of Art Belonging to New York City* (1909).

EXHIBITED: National Sculpture Society, New York, 1898; Pan American Exposition, Buffalo, 1901; Metropolitan Museum, 1918.

PURCHASE, ROGERS FUND, 1922.

Nathan Hale   50.145.38

Nathan Hale (1755–1776), a hero of the Revolutionary War, was captured by the British while acting as a spy and was hanged. He is famous for his last words: "I only regret that I have but one life to lose for my country."

Bronze, height 21½ in. Signed: F. MacMonnies. Dated 1890. Founder's mark: E. Gruet Jeune Fondeur 44 bis Avenue de Chatillon Paris.

REPLICA: City Hall Park, New York (life-size bronze).

REFERENCE: J. W. McSpadden, *Famous Sculptors of America* (1927), pp. 84 f.

EXHIBITED: Paris, Salon of 1891.

BEQUEST OF MARY STILLMAN HARKNESS, 1950.

Other Works

01.11. Medal inscribed: Niagara. 1900(?). Bronze, diameter 1¼ in. Gift of Edward D. Adams, 1901.

33.152.7. Medal commemorating Charles Augustus Lindbergh's transatlantic flight. 1931. Bronze, diameter 2⅞ in. Gift of the Society of Medalists, 1933.

50.145.38

George Grey Barnard
1863-1938

BORN in Bellefonte, Pennsylvania; died in New York. Barnard was the son of a Presbyterian minister. He began his art studies in his youth by training himself in drawing and modeling, but, while working as an expert engraver, decided to become a sculptor. He studied for a year at the Art Institute of Chicago, and in 1883 went to study in Paris. He lived there until 1896, in extreme poverty and loneliness, completely absorbed in his work. In 1894 a number of his works were first exhibited at the Salon du Champ de Mars, where they were highly praised by the French critics, and his principal work, the Struggle of the Two Natures in Man, was purchased for presentation to the Metropolitan Museum. On his return to the United States Barnard taught for a few years at the Art Students League in New York. In 1903 he received a commission for the sculptural decorations of the Pennsylvania State Capitol at Harrisburg. The two large groups designed for this project were made in France between 1903 and 1913.

At this time Barnard began collecting fragments of Gothic and Romanesque sculpture from ruined churches and old farm structures. He brought these to America and set them up in his studio and garden near the present site of Fort Tryon Park. In 1925 this collection was purchased by John D. Rockefeller, Jr., and presented to the Museum as the nucleus of its collection of medieval art, now at The Cloisters. Toward the end of his life Barnard's energies were expended in planning and designing a colossal peace memorial called The Rainbow Arch, which was never completed.

Barnard was one of the few American sculptors of his generation whose marked independence of thought prevented him from falling too deeply into the French academic mold. Some of his more timid and conservative contemporaries considered him a rebel and a dangerous modernist. In fact, he was never quite

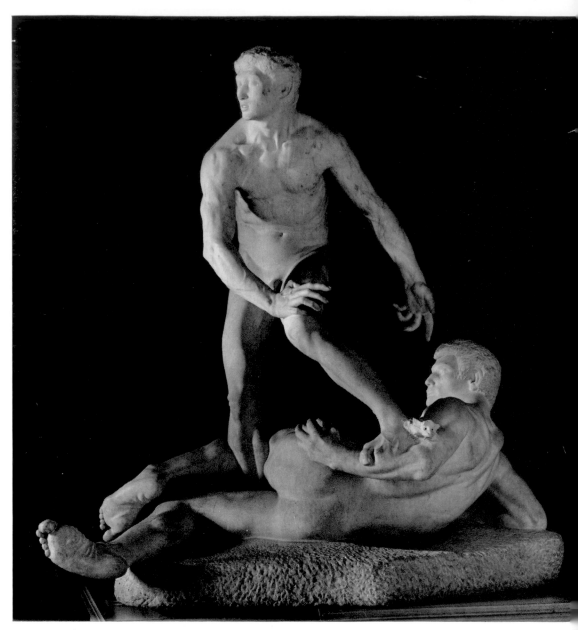

forgiven for his critical triumph in Paris. His statue of Abraham Lincoln (1917) was viciously attacked and derided, as if in retaliation for his having dared to rise to eminence without the assistance and approval of Ruckstull, the secretary of the National Sculpture Society. Barnard was a member of the National Institute of Arts and Letters.

Struggle of the Two Natures in Man
96.11

This statue received its title in 1902 when it was first exhibited at the Museum. It had been referred to as "the group" while Barnard was working on it and had previously been called I Feel Two Natures within Me, a title supposedly suggested by Victor Hugo's poem, "Je sens deux hommes en moi." It reveals Barnard's study of the work of Michelangelo and his rejection of the commonplaces of late nineteenth-century French academic sculpture. Barnard executed all the carving himself—a task few of his contemporaries would have dared to attempt without expert assistance from professional marble-cutters. The clay model was finished in 1889, and the cutting of the marble took more than two years, being completed in 1894.

Of this work the sculptor said: "I was only twenty-one or twenty-two when I did that. . . . I simply expressed my mood at the time. The young man just facing life has no conception of his higher self, his oneness with the Divine. But as soon as he realizes his larger part in the universe, as soon as his sense of immortality is born, then he begins to cast off the earthly and reach up toward the stars."

Marble, height 101½ in.

REPLICAS: Art Institute of Chicago (plaster cast from the marble); Barnard Memorial, Madison, Indiana (plaster). According to the sculptor the original plaster was destroyed.

REFERENCES: W. A. Coffin, *The Century Magazine*, 53 (1897):877; G. P. M., "I Feel Two Natures within Me," *The Congregationalist* (Nov. 3, 1900); C. H. Caffin, *American Masters of Sculpture* (1903); F. W. Coburn, *World*

Today (Mar. 1909); J. W. McSpadden, *Famous Sculptors in America* (1927); L. Taft, *History of American Sculpture* (1930); Babette Deutsch, "Profiles—Sculpture not Machinery," *The New Yorker* (Jan. 17, 1931).

EXHIBITED: Paris, Salon du Champ de Mars, 1894; Logerot Gardens, 2 West 18 Street, New York, 1896; Exposition Universelle, Paris, 1900.

GIFT OF ALFRED CORNING CLARK, 1896.

Abraham Lincoln
29.161

This head was one of the variant portraits made by Barnard when he was commissioned to do a statue of Lincoln to be presented to the city of Cincinnati. The portraits were executed after long study of the life mask of Lincoln taken by Leonard Wells Volk (see p. 28) in 1860. A suggestion that a replica of the statue be given to the city of London aroused bitter criticism of the portrait by arch-conservative sculptors, led by F. Wellington Ruckstull (see p. 61), then editor of *The*

29.161

Art World, a magazine founded to combat the heretical principles of the modern movement. As a result a replica of the tame Saint-Gaudens Lincoln was sent to London instead. Preston Remington wrote of the Barnard head in the Museum's Bulletin, "[It] is beyond question one of the finest portraits of Lincoln yet produced. While emphasizing the vivid physical aspects of the face, the sculptor has also suggested that unselfconsciousness of facial expression which is the inevitable outward reflection of an absence of personal vanity. Despite its undeniable realism Barnard's head of Lincoln is an idealistic portrait of the first order."

95.9

Marble, height 21¼ in. Copyrighted 1919.

REPLICAS: Musée du Luxembourg, Paris; Lincoln School, New York; Los Angeles College (?). Statues in bronze are in Cincinnati; Louisville, Kentucky; and Manchester, England.

REFERENCES: M. F. Roberts, "Lincoln, Soul and Body of Democracy," *Touchstone*, 2 (1917):54; R. Fry, *Burlington Magazine*, 32 (1918):240; P. Remington, *Met. Mus. Bull.*, old series 25 (1930):40, ill.

EXHIBITED: Musée du Luxembourg, Paris, 1919; National Sculpture Society, New York, 1923.

PURCHASE, MORRIS K. JESUP FUND, 1929.

Edmund Austin Stewardson

1865–1892

BORN in Philadelphia; died in Newport, Rhode Island. Stewardson studied at the Pennsylvania Academy of the Fine Arts under Thomas Eakins and later in Paris under Chapu. His first life-size figure, The Bather, was exhibited at the Paris Salon of 1890. Stewardson was drowned in a sailing accident while vacationing in the United States.

The Bather   95.9

The sculptor in a series of letters (beginning in 1889) written to his father from Paris, and published by him, says of his work: "About my figure . . . I have not tried for anything but form . . . I did not want to embarrass myself with any difficulties possible to avoid—it is a first figure, made principally and first of all to learn what 'life size' is, what form really is. . . . It has simply been a useful study of a figure. . . . The French taste in composition or rather arrangement, such as Mr. Chapu's for example, so infinitely ruled, *punished* fairly, to the detriment of real vitality . . . I shall never be able to acquire. . . . Violent action frozen stiff, I dont care a fiddle-stick for, except as a *tour de force*, but concentrated quiet on that account all the more powerful—and beautiful life, is what enthousiasme's me."

The marble was cut from the original plaster by Leonard in Paris in 1894, after the death of the sculptor. The original plaster is in the Pennsylvania Academy of the Fine Arts, Philadelphia.

Marble, height 46 in. Signed: Stewardson. Dated 1891.

REFERENCES: T. Stewardson, *Edmund Stewardson* (privately printed memorial volume, c. 1894); *Catalogue of Sculpture* (Metropolitan Museum, 1908).

EXHIBITED: Paris, Salon of 1890 (plaster), Honorable Mention; Society of American Artists, New York, 1891 (plaster); Louisiana Purchase Exposition, St. Louis, 1904 (lent by Pennsylvania Academy of the Fine Arts).

GIFT OF THOMAS STEWARDSON, 1895.

Richard Edwin Brooks

1865–1919

BORN in Braintree, Massachusetts; died in Boston. For a time Brooks worked with a terra-cotta firm producing architectural sculpture in Boston. He first studied sculpture with Truman H. Bartlett in Boston and after receiving and executing a commission for a portrait bust of Governor Russell was enabled to go to Paris. There he worked in the Académie Colarossi and received instruction from Aubé and Injalbert. The first work he sent to the Salon (1895) was accepted and awarded an Honorable Mention (see Song of the Wave, below). At the Salon of 1899 his work was awarded a Third Class Medal, and at the Paris Exposition in 1900 and the Pan American Exposition in Buffalo in 1901 it received Gold Medals. The state of Maryland commissioned two statues (Charles Carroll and John Hanson) from him, now in the Capitol in Washington. Perhaps his best monumental work was the statue of Thomas Cass, now in the Boston

Public Gardens. Brooks was chairman of the Jury of Awards for Sculpture at the Louisiana Purchase Exposition in St. Louis in 1904. He was a member of the National Sculpture Society (1907) and the National Institute of Arts and Letters.

Song of the Wave   11.103.2

This statuette, made in Paris in 1895, is described by Taft as "a graceful nude female figure presumably seated on the shore of some nameless but sounding sea."

Bronze, height 12½ in. Inscribed: Copyright 1904 by Richard E. Brooks, Paris cire perdue.

REFERENCES: *Met. Mus. Bull.*, old series 6 (1911):179; L. Taft, *History of American Sculpture* (1930).

EXHIBITED: Paris, Salon, 1895 (plaster), Honorable Mention, and 1911 (bronze); Exposition Universelle, Paris, 1900; Society of American Artists, New York, 1905; Pennsylvania Academy of the Fine Arts, Philadelphia, 1907.

PURCHASE, ROGERS FUND, 1911.

The Bather   11.103.1

A small boy testing the temperature of the water at a swimming hole. When this work was first exhibited at the Paris Salon of 1896 it was called Ah! C'est froid (Oh! It's cold).

Bronze, height 23¼ in. Dated 1904. Inscribed: Copyright by Richard E. Brooks Sc et fondeur cire-perdue (11).

REPLICAS: The number (11) marked on this bronze may indicate that there were at least ten other bronze replicas, but none have been located.

REFERENCE: *Met. Mus. Bull.*, old series 6 (1911):179.

EXHIBITED: Paris, Salon, 1896, 1911 (as Baigneur; bronze); Pennsylvania Academy of the Fine Arts, Philadelphia, 1907; National Academy of Design, New York, 1907.

PURCHASE, ROGERS FUND, 1911.

Paul Wayland Bartlett

1865–1925

BORN in New Haven, Connecticut; died in Paris. Although American-born, Paul Bartlett may well be considered a French sculptor since he spent the greater part of his life in Paris. The son of Truman H. Bartlett, the sculptor and author, he was taken to Paris at the age of nine. He received his training as a sculptor of animals under Frémiet and also studied with Cavelier, an old-fashioned sculptor. His precocious talent in modeling secured him a place as an exhibitor at the Salon of 1880 when he was only fifteen years old; at twenty-four he became a member of the Salon jury. Late in his career he came under the influence of the French ceramic sculptor Jean Carriès, who taught him the art of cire-perdue casting and the secrets of managing chemicals to produce iridescent colors on his small bronzes.

Perhaps his best-known works are the Bohemian Bear Tamer (see below), the equestrian statue of Lafayette, in Paris, the statue of Michelangelo in the Library of Congress, and his figures on the façade of the New York Public Library.

Among his many honors was his election to the Legion of Honor, as Chevalier in 1895 and as Commander in 1924. He was a member of the Institut de France, an Associate of the Académie des Beaux-Arts, a member of the National Sculpture Society, the National Institute of Arts and Letters, and the American Academy of Arts and Letters.

Torso of a Woman   09.88.1

Fragment of a standing figure, made about 1895 and cast by Bartlett.

Bronze, height 18½ in.

EXHIBITED: (Some of these may also refer to the following entry.) Paris, Salon, 1895, 1909, 1911; Louisiana Purchase Exposition, St. Louis, 1904; Pennsylvania Academy of the Fine Arts, Philadelphia, 1905; Detroit Museum of Art (now Detroit Institute of Arts), 1907; Baltimore Museum of Art, 1908; Art Institute of Chicago, 1923; Albright Art Gallery, Buffalo, 1923; Musée de l'Orangerie, Paris, *Bartlett Memorial Exhibition*, 1929; American Academy of Arts and Letters, New York, *Bartlett Memorial Exhibition*, 1931.

PURCHASE, ROGERS FUND, 1909.

Torso of a Woman   09.88.2

Fragment of a seated figure, made about 1895 and cast by Bartlett.

Bronze, height 14 in. Signed: Bartlett.

EXHIBITED: (See preceding entry.)

PURCHASE, ROGERS FUND, 1909.

Bohemian Bear Tamer   91.14

Also called The Bohemian and The Bear Trainer (plaster original in the Art Institute of Chicago). The donors provided the information that this statue was awarded a Grand Prix by the International Jury on Sculpture at the Exposition Universelle in 1889. Since the sculptor was a member of the International Jury on Paintings and Drawings, however, he was not allowed to accept the prize, which had been awarded almost unanimously. The gentlemen who gave this piece to the Museum were: S. P. Avery, C. N. Bliss, A. Carnegie, H. O. Havemeyer, R. C. Hawkins, T. Rutter, C. S. Smith, and C. Vanderbilt.

Bronze, height 68½ in. Signed: Paul W. Bartlett. Dated 1887. Founder's mark: Gruet Fondeur Paris.

REPLICA: Boston Museum of Fine Arts (bronze variant, lent by Mary O. Bowditch).

REFERENCES: A. Hoeber, *Treasures of the Metropolitan Museum* (1900); C. H. Caffin, *American Masters of Sculpture* (1903); E. S. Bartlett, *New England Magazine*, 33 (1905): 369; *Catalogue of Sculpture* (Metropolitan Museum, 1908); L. Taft, *History of American Sculpture* (1930).

91.14

EXHIBITED: Paris, Salon, 1887 (as Éleveur d'Ours; plaster), Honorable Mention, and 1888 (bronze, lent by Siot and Perzinka); Exposition Universelle, Paris, 1889, Bronze Medal; World's Columbian Exposition, Chicago, 1893 (plaster); Musée de l'Orangerie, Paris, *Bartlett Memorial Exhibition*, 1929 (bronze reduction); American Academy of Arts and Letters, New York, *Bartlett Memorial Exhibition*, 1931 (bronze reduction).

GIFT OF AN ASSOCIATION OF GENTLEMEN, 1891.

Preparedness   25.72

Statuette of an eagle.

Bronze, height 12½ in. Signed: P. W. Bartlett. Dated 1916. Inscribed: Preparedness.

Copyrighted; founder's mark: Cast by Griffoul, Newark, N.J.

EXHIBITED: Baltimore Museum of Art, 1923 (as American Eagle); American Academy of Arts and Letters, New York, *Bartlett Memorial Exhibition*, 1931 (as The Eagle of Preparedness; catalogue says, "made the day after the sinking of the Lusitania").

GIFT OF THOMAS HENRY RUSSELL AND FREDERICK NEWLIN PRICE, 1925.

Romance—a Study of a Head   19.35

Study for one of the figures designed for the Fifth Avenue façade of the New York Public Library.

Plaster, height 17 in.

REFERENCE: M. Caroll, "Bartlett's Decorative Sculptures for the New York Public Library," *Art and Archaeology*, 3 (1916):35.

GIFT OF PAUL WAYLAND BARTLETT, 1919.

Clinton Ogilvie   20.66

Head of Clinton Ogilvie (1838–1900), American landscape painter.

Marble, height 20 in. Signed: P. W. Bartlett, Sc.

REPLICA: Hall of American Artists, New York University, New York (bronze bust).

REFERENCE: W. Francklyn Paris, *Personalities in American Art* (1930).

GIFT OF MRS. CLINTON OGILVIE, 1920.

John Flanagan
1865–1952

BORN in Newark, New Jersey; died in New York. Flanagan studied at the Cooper Union and modeled architectural ornaments for the Perth Amboy Terra Cotta Works and for Ellin and Kitson, Architectural Sculptors. He worked for three years in Saint-Gaudens's

33.62

Augustus Saint-Gaudens   33.62

According to Flanagan this head was begun in 1905 and abandoned during Saint-Gaudens's final illness in 1907. Work on it was resumed in 1920, and it was finished in 1924.

Bronze, height 16¼ in. Signed: John Flanagan. Dated 1924. Founder's mark: Kunst-Fdry N Y.

REPLICAS: Newark Museum, New Jersey; American Academy of Arts and Letters, New York; Hall of American Artists, New York University, New York; Century Association, New York.

REFERENCE: P. Remington, *Met. Mus. Bull.*, old series 28 (1933):105.

EXHIBITED: Washington, *National Academy of Design Centennial*, 1925; Pennsylvania Academy of the Fine Arts, Philadelphia, 1926; Sesqui-Centennial Exposition, Philadelphia, 1926; National Sculpture Society, San Francisco, 1929; Paris, Salon of 1931.

PURCHASE, FRANCIS LATHROP FUND, 1933.

studio and studied at night in the life classes of George de Forest Brush at the Art Students League. About 1890 he went to Paris and studied at the Académie Julian and Académie Colarossi and in the atelier Falguière of the École des Beaux-Arts. During 1891 he assisted MacMonnies (see p. 82) in constructing the Columbian fountain for the Chicago Exposition. Flanagan received a commission for a clock in the Library of Congress, and was on the staff of the director of fine arts of the United States commission to the Paris Exposition of 1900. He returned to the United States in 1902.

Flanagan was a member of the National Academy of Design, the National Sculpture Society, and the American Numismatic Society. He received awards from the Paris Salon, the National Academy, the Paris Exposition of 1900, the Louisiana Purchase Exposition in 1904, and the Panama Pacific Exposition in 1915. He was best known for his medals, and MacMonnies reportedly considered him the leading medalist of America.

Other Works

09.38.1. Portrait plaquette of Leo Tolstoy. 1907. Copper gilt, 4⅝ x 3½ in. Rogers Fund, 1909.

09.38.2. Portrait medal of Hortense Lenore Mitchell. 1900–1902. Copper gilt, diameter 4¾ in. Rogers Fund, 1909.

09.38.3. Portrait medal of Agnes Lane. 1899. Copper gilt, diameter 4⅝ in. Rogers Fund, 1909.

09.38.4. Portrait medal of Mabel Clarke. 1898. Copper gilt, diameter 4½ in. Rogers Fund, 1909.

09.38.5. Medal of Aphrodite. 1908. Copper gilt, diameter 4⅝ in. Rogers Fund, 1909.

09.196. Medal commemorating the Hudson-Fulton Celebration, with profiles of Henry Hudson and Robert Fulton. 1909. Bronze, diameter 2½ in. Gift of Mr. and Mrs. F. S. Wait, 1909.

11.46. Portrait medal of Dr. Daniel Garrison Brinton. 1898. Bronze, diameter 2½ in. Gift of the Numismatic and Antiquarian Society of Philadelphia, 1911.

33.152.11. Medal of Aphrodite; reverse, Lampededromy (torch race). 1932. Bronze, diameter 2⅞ in. Gift of the Society of Medalists, 1933.

35.16.1. Portrait medal of Joseph Pennell, 1919. Bronze, diameter 4¾ in. Rogers Fund, 1935.

35.16.2. Portrait plaquette of Julian Alden Weir. 1918. Bronze, 5⁷⁄₁₆ x 3¾ in. Rogers Fund, 1935.

50.193. Portrait plaquette of Mark Twain. Inscribed: Mark Twain centenary of his birth MDCCCXXXV-MCMXXXV; Always do right This will gratify some people and astonish the rest. Bronze, 3½ x 2¼ in. Gift of the Society of Medalists, 1950.

Emil Fuchs

1866-1929

BORN in Vienna; died in New York. Fuchs was first trained at the Imperial Academy of Fine Arts in Vienna. Later he went to Berlin to the Royal Academy, and was awarded a scholarship to travel in Italy and study in Rome. In 1897 he went to London, where his work was brought to the attention of the Prince of Wales, later King Edward VII. In England Fuchs was encouraged by his friend John Singer Sargent to attempt portraits in oil, as well as in marble. He came to the United States in 1905 to execute commissions for portraits, and eventually settled permanently in New York and was naturalized. His work as portrait painter, sculptor, medalist, and etcher and his autobiography, *With Pencil, Brush and Chisel, The Life of an Artist* (1925), epitomize the fashionable artist of the extravagant Edwardian era before the first World War. Fuchs died, a suicide, after a serious

illness. In 1931 the Metropolitan Museum received fifteen of his etchings from his estate.

La Pensierosa   19.91

Standing nude woman.

Bronze, height 17¾ in. Signed: Emil Fuchs. Dated 1912. Inscribed: La Pensierosa.

EXHIBITED: Cartier's, New York, 1916.

PURCHASE, ROGERS FUND, 1919.

Other Works

07.83. Coronation medal of King Edward VII and Queen Alexandra. 1901. Bronze, diameter 2½ in. Gift of Emil Fuchs, 1907.

07.84. Medal inscribed: To the memory of those who gave their lives for king and country South African campaign 1899-1902. Bronze, diameter 2¾ in. Gift of Emil Fuchs, 1907.

07.130. Medal commemorating the founding of the Hispanic Society of America. 1906. Silver, diameter 3 in. Gift of the Hispanic Society of America, 1907.

07.296. Portrait medal of Queen Victoria. 1900. Silver, diameter 3 in. Gift of Emil Fuchs, 1907.

09.208.1-9. Nine medals commemorating the Hudson-Fulton Celebration. 1909. Silver, bronze, aluminum, silver-plated, diameters 1¼ - 4 in. Gift of the Medal Committee of the Hudson-Fulton Celebration Commission, 1909.

10.40.9. Medal commemorating the fiftieth anniversary of the American Numismatic Society, 1858-1908. Bronze, diameter 2⅜ in. Gift of Mrs. E. D. Adams, 1910.

13.215. Plaquette in memory of John Pierpont Morgan. 1913. Silver, 2⅞ x 3½ in. 13.226. Bronze duplicate. Gift of Edward D. Adams, 1913.

20.84. Plaquette inscribed: Peace; (reverse) War. Bronze, 2¾ x 1⅞ in. Gift of Pierre C. Cartier, 1920.

22.34.1. Portrait medal of Audrey Hollander. 1921. Silver, diameter 1¼ in. Gift of Barnett L. Hollander, 1922.

22.34.2. Portrait medal of Noel Hollander. 1921. Silver, diameter 1¼ in. Gift of Barnett L. Hollander, 1922.

22.131. Portrait plaquette of Robert Woolston Hunt. Silver, 4 x 2¾ in. Gift of the American Institute of Mining and Metallurgical Engineers, 1922.

Attilio Piccirilli

1866–1945

BORN in Massa di Cararra, Italy; died in New York. Piccirilli was trained in sculpture at the Academy of Saint Luke in Rome, and came to the United States in 1888. He was one of six brothers, all of whom were trained marble workers and all of whom eventually came to New York. With a letter to the Museum written in 1902 he sent a list giving the names, birth dates, and sculptural specialties of each member of the family, beginning with the father, as follows: Giuseppe Piccirilli, born Rome May 16, 1844—carver and pointer; Ferruccio Piccirilli, born Massa May 13, 1864 —ornamental sculptor; Attilio Piccirilli, born Massa May 16, 1866—sculptor; Furio Piccirilli, born Massa March 14, 1868—bas-relief sculptor; Masaniello Piccirilli, born Massa May 18, 1870—ornamental sculptor; Orazio Piccirilli, born Massa May 30, 1872—animal sculptor; Getulio Piccirilli, born Massa May 29, 1874—marble sculptor. In the letter he states further: "My father never was but a very modest marble pointer. All my brothers make their living without the pretension to be called sculptors—they went through the same study as myself."

The arrival of the Piccirilli family in New York may well mark an epoch in the history of American sculpture. Lorado Taft says of them: "Among the best known of the many clever Italians who ply their traditional arts in America is the house of Piccirilli, a family of sculptors and marble cutters who lead in modern New York the life of a Florentine household of the Quattrocento. The great dining room of the establishment is like an old-time refectory, where five stalwart sons with their wives and children gather round a kindly, keen-eyed patriarch. In the large studios adjoining much work is completed in marble for various American sculptors." From the time Daniel Chester French and Herbert Adams discovered the unusual facilities of the Piccirilli Studios this family of sculptors were always busy, and their shop became a central depot from which issued marble copies of many of the most famous works of American sculptors.

The handiwork of the Piccirillis is today to be found in many American museums and on many monuments and public buildings, but it is seldom credited to them. All a sculptor had to do was to present the Piccirillis with a small plaster model of his work; they could enlarge it to any size, cut it in marble and finish it down to the last refinement. It became unnecessary for American sculptors to go to Italy to have their sculpture translated into marble. It became unnecessary, in fact, for a sculptor to know anything about stonecutting, and some were quite content to model in clay and have all their stonework done by the Piccirillis. Some sculptors have been unduly reticent and touchy on this point, but as no one expects an architect actually to build every house he designs or a composer to play every instrument in the orchestra, there seems to be no good reason why this interesting mechanical phase of sculpture should not be better known.

Many sculptural projects were entirely too large for one man to handle alone; for instance, the sculpture of the pediment of the New York Stock Exchange was designed by John Quincy Adams Ward, much of the modeling was done by Paul Bartlett, and the enlarging and stone work were done at the Piccirilli Studios by Getulio Piccirilli. Getulio also enlarged and carved the colossal Lincoln designed by Daniel Chester French for the Lincoln Memorial in Washington. Among the other sculptors who employed the Piccirillis were Paul Bartlett, Frederick MacMonnies, Hermon MacNeil, Massey Rhind, Karl Bitter, Augustus Saint-Gaudens, Olin Warner, Lorado Taft, Charles Niehaus, and Andrew O'Connor. Much of the architectural sculpture done for the architects Cass Gilbert, Henry Bacon, McKim, Mead, and White, Carrère, and Hastings was made at the Piccirilli Studios. The Piccirillis hospitably opened their studios to many sculptors—Calverley, Bartlett, Saint-Gaudens, Warner, French, MacMonnies, and many others—to do their own work there.

Most of the members of the Piccirilli family were so busy cutting the work of other sculptors in stone that they had little time to execute works of their own designing. Attilio, however, was given a number of commissions for monuments, notably the Maine Monument in Central Park, New York, and the Fireman's Monument on Riverside Drive, New York. Attilio was elected a member of the National Academy of Design and the Architectural League, and won a number of prizes and medals, notably a Gold Medal at the Panama Pacific Exposition in San Francisco in 1915.

Study of a Head 19.185

A study of the head of a woman for the allegorical figure Memories, part of a stone group on the Fireman's Monument, Riverside Drive and 100 Street, New York City, dedicated in 1913. This bronze cast was made about 1918.

Bronze, height 20½ in.

REFERENCE: J. V. Lombardo, Attilio Piccirilli, *Life of an American Sculptor* (1944), pp. 134 ff., pls. 31, 33.

EXHIBITED: Metropolitan Museum, 1918; Cincinnati Art Museum, 1918.

PURCHASE, ROGERS FUND, 1919.

26.113

Fragilina 26.113

Figure of a kneeling nude woman, a variant of another work by Attilio Piccirilli, A Soul, made in 1909.

Marble, height 48½ in. Signed: Attilio Piccirilli Fecit. Dated MCMXXIII.

REPLICAS: Two bronzes and a marble are in private collections in New York (the marble was sold at Piccirilli Studio sale, 1949).

REFERENCE: J. V. Lombardo, *Attilio Piccirilli, Life of an American Sculptor* (1944), pp. 155–159.

EXHIBITED: National Sculpture Society, New York, 1923; Architectural League, New York, 1925.

PURCHASE, ROGERS FUND, 1926.

Hermon Atkins MacNeil

1866–1947

BORN in Chelsea, Massachusetts; died in New York. MacNeil studied art at the Massachusetts Normal Art School in Boston and for three years was instructor in modeling at Cornell University. In 1888 he went to study in Paris under Falguière at the École des Beaux-Arts and with Chapu at the Académie Julian. He returned to this country about 1891 and worked as an assistant to Philip Martiny on architectural sculpture for the World's Columbian Exposition in Chicago. After the

Fair he remained in Chicago for three years and made several trips to study the Indians in the far West. In 1895 he married his pupil Carol Brooks. In 1896 he received a Rinehart Roman Scholarship and studied and worked in Rome until 1899. His work was exhibited at the Paris Exposition in 1900, where it was awarded a Silver Medal. On his return to the United States he found employment designing sculptural decorations for the Charleston Exposition in 1902, the St. Louis Exposition in 1904, and the San Francisco Exposition in 1915. Besides this he executed a great many memorial statues and much architectural sculpture; most prominent of these works are the McKinley Memorial, Cleveland, the Ezra Cornell Monument, Ithaca, New York, the Marquette Memorial, Chicago, and the east pediment of the United States Supreme Court Building, Washington. For many years his studio was at College Point, Long Island.

The Sun Vow   19.126

The subject was reputedly inspired by a Sioux initiation ceremony in which the young boys of the tribe, by proving their skill with bow and arrow, are qualified as warriors. The statue was made in 1898. A small version of it was purchased by the Museum in 1906 and disposed of when a large plaster version was acquired in 1917. In 1919, when this large bronze version was purchased, the large plaster was returned to the sculptor.

Bronze, height 73 in. Signed: H. A. MacNeil R.R.S. [Rinehart Roman Scholar], Rome. Inscribed: The Sun-Vow. Founder's mark: Roman Bronze Works, N.Y.

REPLICAS: Montclair Art Museum, New Jersey; Corcoran Gallery of Art, Washington; Art Institute of Chicago; City Art Museum, St. Louis; Brookgreen Gardens, South Carolina; Baltimore Museum of Art; Albright Art Gallery, Buffalo; Wadsworth Atheneum, Hartford, Connecticut; Museum of Arts and Sciences, Norfolk, Virginia; Carnegie Institute, Pittsburgh; Public Museum and Art Gallery, Reading, Pennsylvania.

19.126

39.65.54

REFERENCES: H. W. Chapin, "Hermon Atkins MacNeil," *Pacific Monthly* (Apr. 1906); F. F. Kelly, "American Bronzes at the Metropolitan Museum," *The Craftsman*, 11 (1907): 554; L. Taft, *History of American Sculpture* (1930); B. G. Proske, *Brookgreen Gardens, Sculpture* (1943).

EXHIBITED: Exposition Universelle, Paris, 1900, Silver Medal; Pan American Exposition, Buffalo, 1901, Gold Medal; Art Institute of Chicago, 1901; Society of American Artists, New York, 1901; Pennsylvania Academy of the Fine Arts, Philadelphia, 1902; Louisiana Purchase Exposition, St. Louis, 1904; Metropolitan Museum, 1918; Doll and Richards, Boston, 1919; National Sculpture Society, New York, 1923.

PURCHASE, ROGERS FUND, 1919.

A Chief of the Multnomah Tribe
39.65.54

Originally designed as one of the two Indian figures composing the monument erected in Portland, Oregon, called The Coming of the White Man.

Bronze, height 33⅜ in. Signed: H. A. Mac-Neil. Dated 1905. Inscribed: Multnomah. Founder's mark: R.B.W. [Roman Bronze Works] No. 2.

REPLICAS: According to the sculptor at least twelve bronze casts were made.

REFERENCES: H. W. Chapin, "Hermon Atkins MacNeil," *Pacific Monthly* (Apr. 1906); P. Remington, "The Bequest of Jacob Ruppert," *Met. Mus. Bull.*, old series 34 (1939): 172.

EXHIBITED: Pennsylvania Academy of the Fine Arts, Philadelphia, 1904; Cincinnati Art Museum, 1904; National Sculpture Society, Buffalo (Albright Art Gallery), 1916.

BEQUEST OF JACOB RUPPERT, 1939.

Other Works

33.152.5. Medal inscribed: Hopi; (reverse) Prayer for rain. 1931. Bronze, diameter 2¹³⁄₁₆ in. Gift of the Society of Medalists, 1933.

Amory C. Simons
1866–1959

BORN in Charleston, South Carolina; died in Santa Barbara, California. Simons studied sculpture at the Pennsylvania Academy of the Fine Arts under John J. Boyle, Charles Grafly, and Thomas Eakins. Later he studied in Paris at the Académie Julian under Denys Puech, and also worked with Jean Dampt, Frémiet, Bartlett, and Rodin. Throughout his career he specialized in animal sculpture. His studies of horses won him Honorable Mentions in the Paris Salons of 1900 and

48.167.1

1906, an Honorable Mention at the Pan American Exposition in Buffalo in 1901, a Silver Medal at the Louisiana Purchase Exposition in St. Louis in 1904, and a number of other honors. In 1922 he was awarded the Speyer Prize at the annual exhibition of the National Academy of Design in New York.

Horse Scratching   48.167.1

Made in 1910, cast and patinated by the sculptor.

Bronze, height 9 in.

Exhibited: Baltimore Museum of Art, 1924.

Gift of Amory C. Simons, 1948.

"Haut École"   48.167.2

A performing horse, made in 1910, and cast and patinated by the sculptor.

Bronze, height 14½ in.

Exhibited: Baltimore Museum of Art, 1924.

Gift of Amory C. Simons, 1948.

48.167.2

Karl Bitter

1867–1915

Born in Vienna; died in New York. Bitter was trained as an architectural and decorative sculptor at the School of Applied Art and at the Academy of Fine Arts in Vienna. He came to the United States in 1889 and was employed by a firm of architectural modelers, where his great facility in making decorative sculpture soon came to the attention of the architect Richard Morris Hunt, who adopted Bitter as his protégé. Until Hunt died in 1895, Bitter was constantly employed designing architectural sculpture, fountains, wood carvings, andirons, gates, etc., for Hunt's buildings. His sculptural decorations for Hunt's Administration Building at the World's Columbian Exposition in Chicago in 1893 brought him a national reputation. In 1901 he designed the sculptural decorations for the Fifth Avenue

façade of the Metropolitan Museum—four caryatids representing the arts of painting, sculpture, architecture, and music and six portrait medallions, of Michelangelo, Raphael, Dürer, Velazquez, Rembrandt, and Bramante. Above these were to be four large groups, seated figures symbolizing Egyptian, Greek, Italian renaissance, and modern art; lack of funds and controversy about how modern art should be represented brought this plan to a standstill. Perhaps his best-known work in New York is the Pulitzer Memorial, the so-called Fountain of Abundance, at Fifth Avenue and 59 Street, erected in 1916.

An excellent organizer and planner of large sculptural schemes, Bitter was appointed director of sculpture at three expositions, the Pan American in Buffalo in 1901, the Louisiana Purchase in St. Louis in 1904, and the Panama Pacific in San Francisco in 1915. He died in 1915 as the result of an automobile accident.

Diana   12.50

Standing figure of a nude woman.

Bronze, height 19¼ in. Signed: Karl Bitter. Dated MCMX. Copyrighted; founder's mark: Roman Bronze Works N.Y.

EXHIBITED: National Academy of Design, New York, *Winter Exhibition*, 1910; Art Institute of Chicago, 1911.

PURCHASE, ROGERS FUND, 1912.

Other Works

48.173. Gold cup, designed by Bitter. Made by William Durgin Co., Concord, New Hampshire. 1900 (?). Height 14⁷⁄₁₆ in. Gift of Marcus J. Goldman, 1948.

Edmond Thomas Quinn
1867–1929

BORN in Philadelphia; died in New York. Quinn gave the following information in a

letter to the Museum in 1904 in answer to a request. He studied at the Pennsylvania Academy of the Fine Arts and at the Art Students League in Philadelphia under Thomas Eakins, and in Paris under Injalbert. He made a statue of a kneeling Magdalen in 1900, and a portrait in marble of John Howard in 1902. Quinn also did some painting, mostly portraits.

Among his works is the statue of Edwin Booth in Gramercy Park in New York. Quinn was awarded a Silver Medal at the Panama Pacific Exposition in 1915. He was an Associate of the National Academy of Design, a member of the National Sculpture Society, the New York Architectural League, and the National Institute of Arts and Letters.

Nymph   13.86

A standing nude woman.

Bronze, height 16¼ in. Signed: Quinn. Dated 1912. Copyrighted; founder's mark: Cast by Griffoul Newark N.J.

EXHIBITED: National Academy of Design, New York, *Winter Exhibition*, 1912; Art Institute of Chicago, 1912; Pennsylvania Academy of the Fine Arts, Philadelphia, 1913; Albright Art Gallery, Buffalo, 1913, 1916 (National Sculpture Society), 1919; Panama Pacific Exposition, San Francisco, 1915; Architectural League, New York, 1920; Fine Arts Building, New York, *Retrospective of American Art*, 1921.

PURCHASE, AMELIA B. LAZARUS FUND, 1913.

Charles Oscar Haag
1867–1933

BORN in Norrokoping, Sweden; died in Winnetka, Illinois. Haag studied sculpture in Sweden and later in Paris with Injalbert. He supported himself by designing bronze ornaments for clock cases and worked at this trade in Switzerland, Germany, and France. His life was marked by extreme poverty, and his trade allowed him little spare time for sculpture until he came to the United States in 1902. Knowing the hard lot of craftsmen and designers, he was interested in social democracy and the labor movements of the time, and the themes of much of his sculpture were drawn from the ideas and ideals of these movements.

Accord   06.1227

A peasant man and woman pulling a primitive plough.

Bronze, height 13 in. Signed: Chas. Haag. Dated 1906. Copyrighted; founder's mark: Aubry Bros Founders N.Y.

REFERENCES: C. Eastman, "Charles Haag, Immigrant Sculptor of his Kind," *The Chatauquan*, 48 (1907):249; *Catalogue of Sculpture* (Metropolitan Museum, 1908).

GIFT OF SEVERAL GENTLEMEN, THROUGH JOHN SPARGO, 1906.

Robert Tait McKenzie

1867–1938

BORN in Almonte, Ontario, Canada; died in Philadelphia. McKenzie was educated as a doctor of medicine, graduating from McGill University in 1892. On his graduation he was appointed medical director of physical education and demonstrator in anatomy at McGill. In 1904 he was appointed director of physical education at the University of Pennsylvania, a post he held until his retirement in 1930. His interest in sculpture developed from his medical and anatomical studies. Most of his early sculptures are carefully measured studies of athletes, but later he turned to portraiture and also executed a few monuments. After the first World War McKenzie's specialized knowledge as doctor and sculptor led him into experimentation with plastic surgery for the rehabilitation of soldiers disfigured in the war.

The Competitor   09.56.1

A track athlete tying his shoe.

Bronze, height 20½ in. Signed: R. Tait McKenzie. Dated 1906. Copyrighted; founder's mark: Roman Bronze Works N.Y. No. 5.

REPLICAS: National Gallery of Canada, Ottawa; Springfield College, Springfield, Massachusetts; Yale University Art Gallery, New Haven.

REFERENCE: C. Hussey, *Tait McKenzie; a Sculptor of Youth* (1929).

EXHIBITED: National Academy of Design, New York, *Winter Exhibition*, 1906; Paris, Salon of 1907; Royal Academy, London, 1907; Pennsylvania Academy of the Fine Arts, Philadelphia, 1907; National Sculpture Society, Baltimore, 1908; Albright Art Gallery, Buffalo, 1909; Toronto Art Gallery, 1928.

PURCHASE, ROGERS FUND, 1909.

Other Works

18.50. Medal of the Franklin Institute, award for distinguished service in science. 1914. Bronze, diameter 2½ in. Gift of R. Tait McKenzie, 1918.

36.72.1. Medal with figures symbolizing speed and strength. Reverse inscribed: Rejoice oh young man in thy youth. 1936. Bronze, diameter 2⅞ in. Gift of the Society of Medalists, 1936.

Gutzon Borglum

1867–1941

BORN at Bear Lake in the Idaho Territory; died in Chicago. Borglum studied art at the Mark Hopkins Art Institute in San Francisco in the early 1880's and painted portraits and landscapes in California before going to Paris about 1887. In Paris he studied painting with Lefebvre and Benjamin Constant and sculpture under Mercié at the Académie Julian. Later he spent two years painting in Spain, returning to the United States in 1893. After another trip abroad (when his paintings were sent to Osborne at the command of Queen Victoria for a private viewing), he settled in New York in 1902.

A number of Borglum's sculptural works ornament the Cathedral of Saint John the Divine. Some of these were deliberately smashed by the sculptor in protest, amid much publicity, when theological savants pointed out his grave heretical error in representing some angels as females. Perhaps his best-known works are his colossal carvings on mountains, the Confederate Memorial at Stone Mountain, Georgia, and the Mount Rushmore National Memorial in South Dakota (unfinished at the time of his death). Enormous as these are, they come far short of the staggering dimensions of Borglum's original designs. In these works he achieved the age-old dream of many sculptors who aspired to carve whole mountains—a project many critics thought was better left to nature. In 1914 Borglum galvanized the American art world by stating that most of the public monuments and statues in this country, particularly those in New York and Washington, should be dynamited. He singled out the Washington Monument, the Lincoln Memorial, the National Academy of Design, and the Maine Monument in Central Park, New York, for this drastic treatment. Needless to say, Borglum's outspoken opinions and the gigantic scale of his sculptural projects set him apart from his contemporaries and give him a unique place in the history of American art.

The Mares of Diomedes 06.1318

The classical title and the nude rider cannot disguise the fact that the real subject of this

06.1318

sculpture is a cowboy stampeding a herd of broncos. The allusion to Greek mythology was an afterthought that transformed a cowpoke into Hercules and his ponies into the mythical, flesh-eating mares of the Bistonian king Diomedes.

Bronze (cast by Gorham & Co.), height 62 in. Signed: Gutzon Borglum. Dated 1904. Copyrighted.

REPLICAS: Rhode Island School of Design, Providence (bronze reduction); Brookgreen Gardens, South Carolina (fragment); Musée du Luxembourg, Paris (fragment); Newark Museum, New Jersey (bronze reduction).

REFERENCES: Charles de Kay, *New York Times* (July 10, 1904); Annie Nathan Meyer, *Met. Mus. Bull.*, old series 1 (1906):62; Rupert Hughes, *Appleton's Magazine*, 3 (1906):709; *Catalogue of Sculpture* (Metropolitan Museum, 1908); Elbert Hubbard, *Los Angeles Examiner* (Apr. 26, 1915); J. W. McSpadden, *Famous Sculptors of America* (1927).

EXHIBITED: Louisiana Purchase Exposition, St. Louis, 1904, Gold Medal; Pennsylvania Academy of the Fine Arts, Philadelphia, 1905; National Academy of Design, New York, 1906; National Sculpture Society, Baltimore, 1908 (fragment); Avery Library, Columbia University, New York, 1914.

GIFT OF JAMES STILLMAN, 1906.

06.406

REPLICAS: Rhode Island School of Design, Providence; Detroit Institute of Arts.

REFERENCES: *The Scrip*, 2 (1906):57; *Catalogue of Sculpture* (Metropolitan Museum, 1908); J. W. McSpadden, *Famous Sculptors of America* (1927).

EXHIBITED: Society of American Artists, New York, 1904; Pennsylvania Academy of the Fine Arts, Philadelphia, 1904; Louisiana Purchase Exposition, St. Louis, 1904; Art Institute of Chicago, 1905; National Academy of Design, New York, 1906.

PURCHASE, ROGERS FUND, 1906.

John Ruskin   06.406

Statuette of John Ruskin (1819–1900), British art critic and author. Borglum is reported to have said, "When I saw Ruskin at Windermere he had drawn into himself. He knew his worth. He had full confidence in his own strength, but he was sad. The most marvelous, magnificent, unappreciated genius the world has ever known." (Quoted by McSpadden; see References.)

Bronze, height 15 in. Signed: Gutzon Borglum. Dated 1904. Copyrighted; founder's mark: Gorham Mfg. Co. Founders.

Furio Piccirilli
1868–1949

BORN in Massa di Cararra, Italy; died in Rome. Furio Piccirilli was trained at the Academy of Saint Luke in Rome. He came to the United States with his brothers (see p. 94) in 1888 and worked with them for many years but finally returned to Italy, where he married and settled. His work won Honorable Mention at the Pan American Exposition in Buffalo in 1901 and Silver Medals at the Louisiana Purchase Exposition in St. Louis in 1904 and the Panama Pacific Exposition in San Francisco in 1915. He was a member of the National Academy of Design and an associate of the Architectural League of New York.

Seal   29.103

A black seal balanced on a rock.

Black marble, height 44¾ in. Signed: Furio Piccirilli Fecit. Dated 1927.

REPLICA: Brookgreen Gardens, South Carolina (black marble).

REFERENCES: B. G. Proske, *Brookgreen Gardens, Sculpture* (1943); J. V. Lombardo, *Attilio Piccirilli, Life of an American Sculptor* (1944), p. 281.

EXHIBITED: National Academy of Design, New York, 1929, Speyer Prize.

PURCHASE, ROGERS FUND, 1929.

Solon Borglum

1868–1922

BORN in Ogden, Utah; died in Stamford, Connecticut. Borglum spent the first twenty years of his life on Western ranches, where he learned the ways of Indians and horses. His marked ability to draw horses started him on his career as an artist, in which he was encouraged by his brother Gutzon (see p. 100). Animal sketches made while he was studying at the Cincinnati Art Academy (1895) attracted the attention of the sculptor Rebisso and won him a small scholarship enabling him to go to Paris in 1897. In Paris he attended the Académie Julian and received criticism from the animal sculptor Frémiet and from Puech. His

studies of horses were exhibited in the Salon in 1898 and 1899. He returned to the United States in 1899 and spent the summer on an Indian reservation in the West. His works were awarded Silver Medals at the Paris Exposition in 1900 and at the Pan American Exposition in Buffalo in 1901, and a Gold Medal at the exposition in St. Louis in 1904. Later he established a studio in Silvermine, Connecticut. During the first World War he served with the Y.M.C.A. in France and was in charge of the sculpture department of the American Expeditionary Forces educational system. This work aroused his interest in teaching and led to his founding the American School of Sculpture in New York and to his writing *Sound Construction* (published 1923).

In general, Borglum's monuments are much less successful than his early statuettes of Indians and animals. The influence of Rodin is apparent in his work. He was elected a member of the National Sculpture Society in 1901 and an associate of the National Academy of Design in 1911.

On the Border of the
White Man's Land   07.104

An Indian crouching on a cliff by his pony, made in 1900.

Bronze, height 19 in. Signed: Solon Borglum. Dated 1906. Inscribed: On the Border of the White Man's Land. Copyrighted; founder's mark: Roman Bronze Works N.Y.

REFERENCES: A. Goodrich, "The Frontier in Sculpture," *World's Work*, 3 (1902):1857, ill. showing the sculptural group in Borglum's Paris studio; Frank Sewall, "Sculptor of the Prairie: Solon Borglum," *Century Magazine*, 68 (1904):247; *Catalogue of Sculpture* (Metropolitan Museum, 1908).

EXHIBITED: Exposition Universelle, Paris, 1900, Silver Medal; Pan American Exposition, Buffalo, 1901; Cincinnati Art Museum, 1903 (plaster).

PURCHASE, ROGERS FUND, 1907.

The Bull Fight   07.105

Statuette of two bulls with horns locked in combat, made in 1901.

Bronze, height 4 in. Signed: Solon H. Borglum. Dated 1906. Copyrighted; founder's mark: Roman Bronze Works N.Y.

REPLICA: Brookgreen Gardens, South Carolina.

REFERENCES: A. Goodrich, "The Frontier in Sculpture," *World's Work*, 3 (1902):1857; *Catalogue of Sculpture* (Metropolitan Museum, 1908); B. G. Proske, *Brookgreen Gardens, Sculpture* (1943).

EXHIBITED: Pan American Exposition, Buffalo, 1901; Philadelphia Art Club, 1903; Cincinnati Art Museum, 1903.

PURCHASE, ROGERS FUND, 1907.

Charles Albert Lopez

1869–1906

BORN in Matamoras, Mexico; died in New York. Lopez came to the United States as a young man and worked for a time in the studio of John Quincy Adams Ward. Later he went to Paris and studied at the École des Beaux-Arts under Falguière.

The Sprinter   07.117

This figure was selected by the United States Navy for use as a championship trophy for track and field sports. Specially cast for the Museum in 1907.

Bronze, height 17 in. Signed: Charles Albert Lopez, Sc. Dated 1902. Founder's mark: Roman Bronze Works N.Y.

REPLICA: United States Navy.

REFERENCES: *Catalogue of Sculpture* (Metropolitan Museum, 1908); "Artistic Trophies

for U.S. Navy," *New York Herald* (Nov. 28, 1915).

EXHIBITED: Society of American Artists, New York, 1902; Art Institute of Chicago, 1904, 1912; Louisiana Purchase Exposition, St. Louis, 1904; Pennsylvania Academy of the Fine Arts, Philadelphia, 1905; National Sculpture Society, New York, *Lopez Memorial Exhibition*, 1906; Albright Art Gallery, Buffalo, 1913.

PURCHASE, ROGERS FUND, 1907.

George Dupont Pratt

1869–1935

BORN and died in New York. George Dupont Pratt was elected a Benefactor of the Museum in 1925 in recognition of his many gifts; he was a Trustee of the Museum from 1922 until his death and was for several years Treasurer of the Museum. He was widely known as a patron and collector of art, and his gifts during his lifetime and his collection bequeathed to the Museum enriched many departments, particularly the Department of Near Eastern Art and the Department of Arms and Armor. Pratt was also a Trustee of the American Museum of Natural History and the donor of the George D. Pratt Collection of American Art to Amherst College. He was Treasurer of the American Association of Museums and Vice-President of the Board of Directors of Pratt Institute, founded by his father. His work as a sculptor has been somewhat overshadowed by these and many other philanthropic activities.

Mountain Goat   32.137

Bronze, height 7½ in. Signed: G. D. Pratt. Dated 1914. Copyrighted; founder's mark: Medalic Art Co. N Y.

GIFT OF GEORGE DUPONT PRATT, 1932.

Frances Grimes

1869–

BORN in Braceville, Ohio. Frances Grimes studied sculpture at the Pratt Institute in Brooklyn with Herbert Adams. Later she worked as Adams's studio assistant, and from 1900 until 1907 she was a studio assistant for Augustus Saint-Gaudens.

**Singing Girls—Relief Panels
for a Fountain**   44.44.1,2

Seated nude figures.

Marble, each, height 34 in., width 45 in.

EXHIBITED: Metropolitan Museum, 1918.

GIFT OF JOSEPH PARSONS, 1944.

Lynn Jenkins

1870–1927

Frank Lynn Jenkins. Born in Torquay, England; died in New York. Jenkins studied sculpture at the Lambeth School of Modelling and at the Royal Academy in London. He lived and worked in the United States after 1917.

The Madonna and Child   26.44

Marble, height 18 in. Signed: F. Lynn Jenkins. Dated 1922.

GIFT OF MORTIMER SCHIFF, 1926.

Samuel Murray

1870–1941

BORN and died in Philadelphia. Murray entered the Philadelphia Art Students League in 1887, then recently organized by the painter Thomas Eakins. He rapidly became Eakins's favorite pupil, and for a number of years they shared the same studio. Most of Murray's works are in Pennsylvania. They include the Pennsylvania State Monument in Gettysburg and various portrait statues erected in Philadelphia. Murray was instructor in modeling at the Moore Institute and the Philadelphia School of Design for Women.

23.155

Thomas Eakins   23.155

Portrait statuette of the American painter and teacher Thomas Eakins (1844-1916).

Bronze, height 9 in. Signed: Murray. Dated 1907. Copyrighted; founder's mark: Roman Bronze Works N.Y.

REFERENCE: *American Art Annual*, 13 (1916): 312, ill. (photograph: "Thomas Eakins . . . Regarding a Statuette of Himself by Samuel Murray").

EXHIBITED: Pennsylvania Academy of the Fine Arts, Philadelphia, 1898; Louisiana Purchase Exposition, St. Louis, 1904; National Academy of Design, New York, 1908; Concord Art Association, Concord, Massachusetts, 1922; National Sculpture Society, New York, 1923; Century Association, New York, 1923.

PURCHASE, ROGERS FUND, 1923.

22.89

22.154

A. Stirling Calder
1870–1945

Alexander Stirling Calder. Born in Philadelphia; died in New York. Calder was the son of the sculptor Alexander Milne Calder. As a young man he studied at the Pennsylvania Academy of the Fine Arts under Thomas Eakins and Thomas Anshutz. At the age of twenty he went to Paris and studied at the École des Beaux-Arts and the Académie Julian, where he received instruction from Chapu and Falguière. On his return to Philadelphia he became a teacher at the Pennsylvania Academy; in later years he taught at the Art Students League and the National Academy of Design in New York.

Calder's work was exhibited at the Pan American Exposition in Buffalo in 1901, the Louisiana Purchase Exposition in St. Louis in 1904, the Alaska-Yukon Pacific Exposition in Seattle in 1909, and the Panama Pacific Exposition in San Francisco in 1915, where Calder was Acting Director of the Department of Sculpture. A number of his works have been placed in Fairmount Park, Philadelphia, among them the Swann Memorial Fountain at Logan Circle. All his work is marked by a curious and very individual style. Calder was a member of the National Sculpture Society, the National Institute of Arts and Sciences, and the National Academy of Design.

Man Cub   22.89

A nude boy about four years old, a portrait of the sculptor's son, made around 1901.

Bronze, height 44 in. Signed: Calder.

REPLICA: Pennsylvania Academy of the Fine Arts, Philadelphia.

EXHIBITED: Pennsylvania Academy of the Fine Arts, Philadelphia, 1902, 1906; Louisiana Purchase Exposition, St. Louis, 1904, Silver Medal; Metropolitan Museum, 1918; Musée du Luxembourg, Paris, 1920.

PURCHASE, ROGERS FUND, 1922.

Scratching Her Heel   22.154

Figure of a nude woman, probably made about 1920.

Bronze, height 12 in. Signed: Calder. Founder's mark: Roman Bronze Works N.Y.

EXHIBITED: Fine Arts Building, New York, *Retrospective of American Art*, 1921; National Sculpture Society, New York, 1923; Albright Art Gallery, Buffalo, 1924; Brooklyn Museum, New York, 1930.

PURCHASE, ROGERS FUND, 1922.

Other Works

38.111.1. Medal inscribed: The dance of life begins early and goes on; (reverse) With pleasure pain and the protagonist. 1938. Bronze, diameter 2½ in. Gift of the Society of Medalists, 1938.

Adolph Alexander Weinman

1870–1952

BORN in Karlsruhe, Germany; died in Portchester, New York. Weinman was brought to the United States in 1880. As a youth he was apprenticed to a carver of wood and ivory. He studied at the Cooper Union and the Art Students League in New York and under Augustus Saint-Gaudens and Philip Martiny, and worked as a studio assistant with Charles Niehaus, Olin Warner, and Daniel Chester French. Weinman designed the United States dime and half dollar of 1916. However, he was most well known for his architectural sculpture. He was a member of the Architectural League of New York and the National Academy of Design.

Abraham Lincoln   13.196

This statuette was designed in 1911 as a study for the Lincoln Monument in Frankfort, Ken-

tucky, and presented to the state of Kentucky by James Breckenridge Speed.

Bronze, height 25 in. Signed: A. A. Weinman. Dated MCMXI.

EXHIBITED: National Sculpture Society, New York, 1913.

GIFT OF MR. AND MRS. JAMES BRECKENRIDGE SPEED, 1913.

Other Works

07.251.76. Medal of the Louisiana Purchase Exposition. 1904. Bronze, diameter 2½ in. Gift of Mr. and Mrs. F. S. Wait, 1907. 08.7. Duplicate. Gift of Clarence Hoblitzelle, 1907.

20.159. Medal of Mount Sinai Hospital. 1920. Bronze, diameter 3 in. Gift of the Trustees of Mount Sinai Hospital through George Blumenthal, 1920.

49.77.1. Medal inscribed: Genesis; (reverse) Web of destiny. 1949. Bronze, diameter 2⅞ in. Gift of the Society of Medalists, 1949.

Edith Woodman Burroughs

1871–1916

BORN in Riverdale, New York; died in Flushing, New York. Edith Woodman's serious art studies began at the age of fifteen when she entered the drawing classes of Kenyon Cox and the modeling classes of Augustus Saint-Gaudens at the Art Students League in New York. Later she studied in Paris under Injalbert and Merson. She married the painter Bryson Burroughs in 1893. On a trip to Paris in 1909 she came under the influence of the French sculptor Maillol. Mrs. Burroughs designed two fountains for the Panama Pacific Exposition in San Francisco in 1915. She was a member of the National Sculpture Society and an Associate of the National Academy of Design. A commemorative exhibition of her sculpture was held by the National Sculpture Society after her death.

10.199

John La Farge   10.199

Bust of La Farge (1835–1910), the American artist, author, and teacher, made in 1908.

Bronze, height 16½ in. Signed: Edith Woodman Burroughs. Founder's mark: C. Valsuani Cire Perdue.

EXHIBITED: National Academy of Design, New York, *Winter Exhibition*, 1908; Berlin Photographic Co., New York, 1915; National Sculpture Society, Buffalo (Albright Art Gallery), 1916.

PURCHASE, ROGERS FUND, 1910.

At the Threshold   20.76

This figure of a nude girl, made in 1912, is described in the catalogue of the 1915 exhibition of Mrs. Burroughs' sculpture as a "young girl of twelve or thirteen who looks out on womanhood with wondering dull eyes."

Limestone, height 62½ in. Signed: Edith Woodman Burroughs.

REFERENCE: *Sculptures by Edith Woodman Burroughs* (exhibition cat., Berlin Photographic Co., 1915) (Introduction by Bryson Burroughs).

EXHIBITED: Berlin Photographic Co., New York, 1915; National Sculpture Society, Buffalo (Albright Art Gallery), 1916; Metropolitan Museum, 1918.

EX COLL. Bryson Burroughs, New York.

PURCHASE, AMELIA B. LAZARUS FUND, 1919.

Other Works

09.116. Portrait medal of Edgar Allan Poe, Grolier Club Memorial. 1909. Bronze, diameter 6⅞ in. Gift of R. T. H. Halsey, 1909.

16.125. Portrait medal of Roger Fry. 1911. Bronze, diameter 4⅝ in. Gift of Bryson Burroughs, 1916.

Henry Merwin Shrady

1871–1922

BORN and died in New York. Shrady was the son of a well-to-do physician and was educated as a lawyer at Columbia University. As an artist he was entirely self-taught and specialized in painting and modeling studies of animals. For a time he worked in the studio of the sculptor Karl Bitter. Shortly after beginning his career as a sculptor, he was awarded a $250,000 commission for the Appomattox Memorial Monument to General Grant in Washington. Shrady's design was selected from models sent in by fifty-two contestants by a jury of award consisting of Augustus Saint-Gaudens, Charles F. McKim, and Daniel Chester French. Work on this vast undertaking occupied nineteen years of the sculptor's life, and the completed monument was unveiled shortly after his death. It is believed that the Grant Monument commission was awarded to the unknown Shrady amid much politicking to prevent Niehaus from getting it.

A Bull Moose   48.149.25

This statuette, enlarged to life size in plaster, was used to ornament the bridges erected in the grounds of the Pan American Exposition in Buffalo in 1901.

Bronze, height 19½ in. Founder's mark: Copyrighted 1900 Theodore B. Starr, Serial No. 5.

BEQUEST OF GEORGE DUPONT PRATT, 1935.

Cavalry Charge   25.75

This cast was made in 1924 from the quarter-size model of a design for one of the groups at the base of the equestrian statue of General Grant in the Appomattox Memorial Monument in Washington.

Bronze, height 53½ in. Signed: Henry-Merwin Shrady. Founder's mark: Cast by Roman Bronze Works N Y.

REFERENCES: B. Church, *Journal of American History*, 7 (1913):1005; H. Wright, "The Grant Memorial in Washington," *Art and Archaeology*, 12 (1922):185.

EXHIBITED: National Sculpture Society, New York, 1923 (plaster).

GIFT OF MRS. HELEN FAHNESTOCK CAMPBELL, 1925.

Alfred David Lenz

1872–1926

BORN in Fond du Lac, Wisconsin; died in Havana, Cuba. Lenz was the son of a skilled wood-carver. He was trained in watchmaking; as a sculptor he was self-taught. His earliest work in sculpture was a portrait bust of the Reverend Judson Titsworth of Milwaukee. In 1893 Lenz went to London and Paris, and on his return to this country he became a designer for a firm of manufacturing jewelers in New York. In connection with this work he became interested in perfecting new casting methods for use with precious metals. Most of his works are small figurines cast in precious metals; these fall into a special class of work somewhere between sculpture and jewelry and earned for the artist the title of "the modern Cellini." The Architectural League of New York awarded him a Gold Medal in 1925. After his death a memorial exhibition of his work was held in Milwaukee.

Lenz bequeathed detailed descriptions of his casting processes to the National Sculpture

Society, and they have been published by the Society for the benefit of sculptors and students of fine metalwork. The titles of some of his works are: Atalanta's Race, Aphrodite, Snake Charmer, Ennui, Lady Buggs, Bacchante, Head of Beethoven, Spirit of the Dance, Star Dust, Senorita Hooch. Most of these are very small in scale and worked in great detail; some are cast in gold and silver and ornamented with pearls, gem stones, and enamel, relating them more closely to jewelry than to sculpture in the usual sense.

The Dragonfly—Pavlova   20.17

Portrait statuette, probably cast by Lenz, of the Russian dancer Anna Pavlova (1885–1931)

20.17

as The Dragonfly. The drapery is arranged to support the figure in mid-air.

Bronze, height 8 in. Signed: Lenz. Dated 1916, New York. Copyrighted.

EXHIBITED: Architectural League, New York, 1919–1920; National Academy of Design, New York, *Winter Exhibition*, 1920; Pennsylvania Academy of the Fine Arts, Philadelphia, 1920 (lent by the Metropolitan Museum).

PURCHASE, ROGERS FUND, 1920.

Frederick George Richard Roth

1872–1944

BORN in Brooklyn, New York; died in Englewood, New Jersey. Roth was educated in Germany and studied sculpture with Edmund von Hellmer at the Academy of Fine Arts in Vienna and with Meyerheim at the Royal Academy in Berlin. His reputation was established in this country by his Roman Chariot Race at the Pan American Exposition in Buffalo in 1901 and by his studies of animals. He also designed architectural sculpture for the Louisiana Purchase Exposition in St. Louis in 1904 and for the Panama Pacific Exposition in San Francisco in 1915. From 1934 to 1936 he was chief sculptor of the Department of Parks in New York City under the Works Progress Administration. He was president of the National Sculpture Society and a member of the Architectural League of New York and the National Institute of Arts and Letters.

Polar Bear   06.400

Bronze, height 7½ in. Signed: Fred G. R. Roth. Dated 1903. Copyrighted; founder's mark: Roman Bronze Works N Y.

REFERENCE: *Catalogue of Sculpture* (Metropolitan Museum, 1908).

EXHIBITED: Louisiana Purchase Exposition, St. Louis, 1904; Pennsylvania Academy of the

06.401

06.402

Fine Arts, Philadelphia, 1905; Albright Art Gallery, Buffalo, 1912, and 1916 (National Sculpture Society); Panama Pacific Exposition, San Francisco, 1915.

PURCHASE, ROGERS FUND, 1906.

Performing Elephants 06.401,402

Companion pieces.

Bronze, height 6 in. Signed: F. G. R. Roth. Dated 1902. Copyrighted; founder's mark: Roman Bronze Works N Y Serial Nos. M 1 N 11, M 2 N 12.

REFERENCES: C. Caffin, *American Masters of Sculpture* (1903); *Catalogue of Sculpture* (Metropolitan Museum, 1908).

EXHIBITED: Albright Art Gallery, Buffalo, 1909.

PURCHASE, ROGERS FUND, 1906.

Performing Bear 06.403

Bronze, height 9½ in. Signed: F. G. R. Roth. Dated 1903. Copyrighted; founder's mark: Roman Bronze Works N Y.

REFERENCE: *Catalogue of Sculpture* (Metropolitan Museum, 1908).

PURCHASE, ROGERS FUND, 1906.

Pig Tied to a Stake and Pig Scratching 06.404, 405

Companion pieces.

Bronze, height 3½ in. Signed: Fred G. R. Roth. Dated 1903. Copyrighted; founder's mark: Roman Bronze Works N Y Serial Nos. M 1 N 5, M 2 N 5.

REFERENCE: *Catalogue of Sculpture* (Metropolitan Museum, 1908).

PURCHASE, ROGERS FUND, 1906.

06.404

Tricky Patterboots Clark—
Portrait of a Dog   10.115

Bronze, height 5½ in. Signed: F. G. R. Roth
fec. Dated 1910. Inscribed: Tricky Patter-
boots Clark. Founder's mark: Roman Bronze
Works N Y.

GIFT OF MISS MABEL E. CLARK, 1910.

Bessie Potter Vonnoh

1872–1955

BORN in St. Louis; died in New York. Bessie
Potter first studied art with Lorado Taft at
the Art Institute of Chicago, and assisted Taft
on the decorations for the Columbian Exposition of 1893. She traveled abroad to Paris
in 1895 and to Florence in 1897, but never
studied in a school there or under a European

master. After marrying the painter Robert
Vonnoh in 1899, she made her home in New
York.

She received awards at the Paris Salon in
1900, the Louisiana Purchase Exposition in
St. Louis in 1904, the Panama Pacific Exposition in 1915, and the National Academy of
Design in 1921. She was a member of the National Sculpture Society, the National Academy of Design, and the National Institute of
Arts and Letters.

The Young Mother   06.306

Statuette of a mother and child.

Bronze, height 14½ in. Signed: Bessie O.
Potter. Dated 1896. Copyrighted; founder's
mark: Roman Bronze Works N.Y. Serial No.
VI.

REPLICAS: Brooklyn Museum, New York;
Art Institute of Chicago; Montclair Art Museum, New Jersey; Fine Arts Gallery of San
Diego. According to the sculptor thirty examples were cast in bronze.

REFERENCE: *Catalogue of Sculpture* (Metropolitan Museum, 1908).

EXHIBITED: Pennsylvania Academy of the
Fine Arts, Philadelphia, 1896; Society of
American Artists, New York, 1897; Exposi-
tion Universelle, Paris, 1900, Bronze Medal;
Pan American Exposition, Buffalo, 1901;
Louisiana Purchase Exposition, St. Louis,
1904; Cincinnati Art Museum, 1905, 1911;
National Sculpture Society, Baltimore, 1908;
Montross Gallery, New York, 1913; Panama
Pacific Exposition, San Francisco, 1915.

PURCHASE, ROGERS FUND, 1906.

Girl Dancing   06.305

Sometimes called The Dance.

Bronze, height 14 in. Signed: Bessie O. Potter.
Dated 1897. Copyrighted; founder's mark:
Roman Bronze Works N Y Serial No. X.

REPLICAS: Brooklyn Museum, New York;
Art Institute of Chicago; American Academy
of Arts and Letters, New York; Newark Mu-

seum, New Jersey; Carnegie Institute, Pittsburgh; Rochester Athenaeum, New York. According to the sculptor forty-five bronzes were cast.

REFERENCE: *Catalogue of Sculpture* (Metropolitan Museum, 1908).

EXHIBITED: Pennsylvania Academy of the Fine Arts, Philadelphia, 1899; Exposition Universelle, Paris, 1900; Cincinnati Art Museum, 1904; Albright Art Gallery, Buffalo, 1909, and 1916 (National Sculpture Society); Art Institute of Chicago, 1912; Paris, Salon of 1912; Armory Show, New York, 1913; Montross Gallery, New York, 1913; Panama Pacific Exposition, San Francisco, 1915.

PURCHASE, ROGERS FUND, 1906.

His First Journey   06.307

Statuette of a creeping infant.

Bronze, height 4¾ in. Signed: Bessie Potter Vonnoh. Dated 1901. Founder's mark: Roman Bronze Works N.Y. Serial No. X.

REPLICAS: According to the sculptor thirty-nine bronze casts were made.

REFERENCE: *Catalogue of Sculpture* (Metropolitan Museum, 1908).

EXHIBITED: Art Institute of Chicago, 1903; Cincinnati Art Museum, 1904; National Academy of Design, New York, 1905; National Sculpture Society, Baltimore, 1908, Buffalo (Albright Art Gallery), 1916, and New York, 1923; Montross Gallery, New York, 1913; Panama Pacific Exposition, San Francisco, 1915.

PURCHASE, ROGERS FUND, 1906.

Enthroned   06.298

Statuette of a mother and three children, made in 1902.

Bronze, height 11½ in. Signed: Bessie Potter Vonnoh. Founder's mark: Roman Bronze Works N Y, Serial No. VI.

REPLICAS: Brooklyn Museum, New York; Corcoran Gallery of Art, Washington. According to the sculptor twenty-one bronze casts were made.

REFERENCE: *Catalogue of Sculpture* (Metropolitan Museum, 1908).

EXHIBITED: Pennsylvania Academy of the Fine Arts, Philadelphia, 1904; Society of American Artists, New York, 1904, Shaw Memorial Prize; Albright Art Gallery, Buffalo, 1909, and 1916 (National Sculpture Society); Montross Gallery, New York, 1913; Panama Pacific Exposition, San Francisco, 1915.

GIFT OF GEORGE A. HEARN, 1906.

Arthur Putnam
1873–1930

BORN in Waveland, Mississippi; died in Paris. As a sculptor Putnam was almost entirely self-taught. In 1894 he had some training at the San Francisco Art Students League and for a time he worked with the animal sculptor Kemeys in Chicago, but he could not stand life in the city and returned to California in 1899 to be married. At this time he was living in extreme poverty, but about 1905 he was enabled to go to Italy and France by the interest of a member of the Crocker family, who bought some of his bronzes. When his work was exhibited in Paris in 1906 and 1907 it was received very favorably, but again Putnam's hatred of life in the city drove him back to California. Here he earned a living by doing architectural sculpture. In 1909 he started a bronze foundry, which was fairly successful, but in this year he began to suffer from a brain tumor. An operation left him paralyzed and quite changed in character. From that time forward he did no important work in sculpture. In 1917 he went to Paris to live with his second wife, remaining there until his death. He was one of the most promising young sculptors of his time, and Rodin is said to have exclaimed on being shown Putnam's animal studies, "This is the work of a master!"

Snarling Jaguar   09.81

Bronze, height 2¾ in. Signed: Putnam. Dated '06. Copyrighted; founder's mark: Putnam and Storey Founders S.F. Cal.

REPLICAS: California Palace of the Legion of Honor, San Francisco; Fine Arts Gallery of San Diego, California.

EXHIBITED: Paris (?); Macbeth Galleries, New York, 1909 (?).

PURCHASE, ROGERS FUND, 1909.

Janet Scudder

1873–1940

BORN in Terre Haute, Indiana; died in Rockport, Massachusetts. Janet Scudder studied at the Cincinnati Art Academy under Rebisso and later earned her living as a wood-carver in Chicago before entering the studio of Lorado Taft. Here she became one of the group of lady assistants known as "the White Rabbits" who worked with Taft on his sculptural projects for the World's Columbian Exposition in 1893. Later she went to Paris to study with Frederick MacMonnies. Her reputation was established when Stanford White purchased two copies of her Frog Fountain to use in the gardens of his clients, though she was rather coolly received as a rival by French and Saint-Gaudens in spite of the fact that she specialized in making fountains of a type that neither of them was interested in. Miss Scudder lived for many years in France and in 1925 was made a Chevalier of the Legion of Honor in recognition of her work during the first World War. At the Paris Salon of 1911 her sculpture was awarded Honorable Mention. She was the first American woman sculptor to have her portrait medallions accepted by the Musée du Luxembourg.

The Frog Fountain   06.967

In her autobiography Miss Scudder devoted a whole chapter to her Frog Fountain, made in Paris in 1901, which marked the beginning of her success as a sculptor of fountains. In an earlier chapter she tells of the first time the little boy who posed for it came to her Paris studio: "In that moment a finished work flashed before me. I saw a little boy dancing, laughing, chuckling all to himself while a spray of water dashed over him. The idea of my Frog Fountain was born." When it was finished Miss Scudder asked MacMonnies for his criticism: "It's amusing!" he said at last. "Awfully amusing!" "That's what I meant it to be. That is what my work is going to be from now on." He smiled approval. "What are you going to do with it?" "Take it to New York—and start out on my career of designing fountains for gardens—for courtyards—for terraces."

Bronze, height 37½ in. Signed: Janet Scudder. Founder's mark: E. Gruet Jne. Fondeur Paris.

REPLICAS: Brookgreen Gardens, South Carolina (small bronze). According to the sculptor four life-size bronzes were cast, and the original plaster was destroyed. One replica was made in marble. With the exception of the bronze now in this Museum they are all in the gardens of private estates.

REFERENCES: *Catalogue of Sculpture* (Metropolitan Museum, 1908); Janet Scudder, *Modeling My Life* (1925); C. Baldwin,*Stanford White* (1930); B. G. Proske, *Brookgreen Gardens, Sculpture* (1943).

EXHIBITED: Paris, Salon, 1905, 1910; National Sculpture Society, Baltimore, 1908, and Buffalo (Albright Art Gallery), 1916; Pennsylvania Academy of the Fine Arts, Philadelphia, 1909; Cincinnati Art Museum, 1909, 1918; Panama Pacific Exposition, San Francisco, 1915; Albright Art Gallery, Buffalo, 1918; National Academy of Design, New York, 1918; Sesqui-Centennial Exposition, Philadelphia, 1926.

PURCHASE, ROGERS FUND, 1906.

Other Works

06.1331.1. Portrait plaquette of Caroline Reeves Foulke. 1904. Silvered copper, 5¼ x 3¾ in. Rogers Fund, 1906.

06.1331.2. Portrait plaquette of Alice. 1906. Silver, 4⅜ x 3¼ in. Rogers Fund, 1906.

06.1331.3. Portrait plaquette of Percy Chubb. 1903. Silvered copper, 4⁷⁄₁₆ x 3⁵⁄₁₆ in. Rogers Fund, 1906.

06.1331.4. Portrait plaquette of Silas Weir Mitchell. 1909. Silvered copper, 3⅝ x 2⅞ in. Rogers Fund, 1906.

09.20.1. Portrait plaquette of Royal Parsons. 1906. Silvered copper, 4¼ x 2½ in. Rogers Fund, 1909.

09.20.2. Portrait plaquette of Mildred Barnes. 1906. Silvered copper, 4⅜ x 3⅝ in. Rogers Fund, 1909.

09.20.3. Portrait plaquette of Helen Seely. 1906. Silvered copper, 5¼ x 2³⁄₁₆ in. Rogers Fund, 1909.

09.20.4. Portrait medallion of Master Billy Fahnestock. 1904. Silvered copper, diameter 6¼ in. Rogers Fund, 1909.

Henri Crenier

1873-1948

BORN in Paris; died in New York. As a young man Crenier studied under Falguière at the École des Beaux-Arts. His work was exhibited regularly at the Salons from 1892 until 1902, when he came to the United States and found employment as an architectural sculptor. His most notable architectural works are the decorations of the San Francisco City Hall.

Fountain— Boy and Turtle

13.87

This fountain was modeled in 1912. A life-size version is in Mount Vernon Place, Baltimore, Maryland.

Bronze, height 19½ in. Signed: H. Crenier. Founder's mark: Roman Bronze Works N.Y.

REPLICAS: Mount Vernon Place, Baltimore, Maryland (life size). Several unlocated replicas were cast in the small size and sold through the firm of Theodore B. Starr, Inc.

REFERENCE: W. S. Rusk, *Art in Baltimore* (1924).

EXHIBITED: National Academy of Design, New York, 1912–1913 (?); Art Institute of Chicago, 1912; Albright Art Gallery, Buffalo, 1913; Architectural League, New York, 1916, 1917; National Sculpture Society, Buffalo (Albright Art Gallery), 1916, and New York, 1923; Baltimore Museum of Art, 1923.

PURCHASE, AMELIA B. LAZARUS FUND, 1913.

Andrew O'Connor, Jr.

1874-1941

BORN in Worcester, Massachusetts; died in Dublin, Ireland. At the age of fourteen, Andrew O'Connor was working on monuments for cemeteries under the direction of his father. Later he worked as studio assistant for William Ordway Partridge in Chicago, and for Daniel Chester French in New York. His work brought him to the attention of the architect Stanford White, and he was frequently employed by the firm of McKim, Mead, and White to do architectural sculpture. O'Connor studied with Sargent in London and with Rodin in Paris. He received a Bronze Medal at the Panama Pacific Exposition in 1901 and a Second Class Medal at the Paris Salon of 1906. Several of his works were purchased by the French government for the Luxembourg Museum. He designed the Vanderbilt Memorial doors for St. Bartholomew's Church in New York and an equestrian statue of Lafayette in Baltimore. In 1919 O'Connor was made an associate member of the National Academy.

Head of the Virgin

18.38

According to the sculptor this bronze, specially cast for the Museum in 1909, was the only one made. The original was modeled in 1906.

18.38

Bronze, height 18 in. Signed: O'Connor.

EXHIBITED: International Art Exposition, Venice, 1910; Glaenzer Gallery, New York, 1917; Metropolitan Museum, 1918; Albright Art Gallery, Buffalo, 1919.

PURCHASE, ROGERS FUND, 1918.

Abraham Lincoln   22.14

This bust of Lincoln (1807–1865), cut in stone in 1916 from a model made in 1915, is a variant after the model for the Lincoln Monument in Springfield, Illinois.

Limestone, height 38 in.

REPLICAS: Whitney Museum of American Art, New York (bronze head); Art Institute of Chicago; Royal Exchange, London.

EXHIBITED: National Sculpture Society, New York, 1923.

GIFT OF MRS. WILLARD D. STRAIGHT, 1922.

Evelyn Beatrice Longman
1874–1954

Mrs. Nathaniel Horton Batchelder. Born in Winchester, Ohio; died in Osterville, Massachusetts. At the age of fourteen, Evelyn Longman was working in a wholesale house and attending evening classes at the Art Institute of Chicago. She saved her money for seven years to go to Olivet College, Olivet, Michigan, but after a year and a half there, left to enroll in Lorado Taft's sculpture courses at the Art Institute of Chicago. In 1900 she went to New York, where she assisted Mac-Neil and Konti on the decorations for the Pan American Exposition in Buffalo in 1901. She was the only woman ever admitted as an assistant to the studio of Daniel Chester French, where she worked for three years until she began an independent career. Like French, she did much of her work in collaboration with the architect Henry Bacon.

Among her many awards are the Watrous Gold Medal in 1923, the Shaw Prize in 1918 and 1926, the W.M.R. French Gold Medal in 1920, and the Widener Gold Medal in 1921. She was a member of the Connecticut Academy of Fine Arts, the National Sculpture Society, and the American Numismatic Society. She was the first woman sculptor ever to be elected a full member of the National Academy of Design.

Victory   12.143

This figure of a man in classical dress holding aloft a laurel wreath and an oak branch was originally designed and used as a finial on the dome of the Festival Hall at the Louisiana Purchase Exposition in St. Louis in 1904. A small-size replica was later chosen for a trophy awarded in athletic competition by the Atlantic Fleet of the United States Navy. The movement to substitute bronze figures by American sculptors for the traditional "cup" trophies was instituted by Edward Holbrook, president of Gorham Company.

Bronze, height 30¼ in. Signed: Evelyn B. Longman. Dated 1903. Founder's mark: Roman Bronze Works N.Y. No. 1.

REPLICAS: Brookgreen Gardens, South Carolina; John Herron Art Institute, Indianapolis; Toledo Museum of Art; private collection, New York; City Art Museum, St. Louis (large size); Union League Club, Chicago (large size); Atlantic Fleet, United States Navy. According to the sculptor about thirty-five small-size replicas and at least two in a larger size were cast in bronze.

REFERENCES: "Artistic Trophies for U.S. Navy," *New York Herald* (Nov. 28, 1915); B. G. Proske, *Brookgreen Gardens, Sculpture* (1943).

EXHIBITED: Louisiana Purchase Exposition, St. Louis, 1904; Architectural League, New York, 1904; Pennsylvania Academy of the Fine Arts, Philadelphia, 1905; Art Institute of Chicago, 1905, 1912; National Academy of Design, New York, 1912.

GIFT OF EDWARD D. ADAMS, 1912.

Louise   20.55

Portrait bust of a young girl (Louise French), modeled about 1904.

Tinted marble, height 21½ in. Signed: Evelyn Beatrice Longman, Sc. Dated 1910.

REPLICAS: Private collection, Bangor, Maine (plaster); private collection, Saratoga Springs, New York (plaster).

EXHIBITED: Pennsylvania Academy of the Fine Arts, Philadelphia, 1904; Art Institute of Chicago, 1905, 1913; National Academy of Design, 1912; Metropolitan Museum, 1918 (marble).

PURCHASE, ROGERS FUND, 1920.

12.143

A Torso   12.52

Seated figure of a nude woman.

Bronze, height 13¼ in. Signed: Evelyn Beatrice Longman. Dated 1911. Founder's mark: Roman Bronze Works N.Y.

REPLICAS: Private collection, New York; City Art Museum, St. Louis. According to the sculptor only three bronze casts were made.

EXHIBITED: National Academy of Design, New York, *Winter Exhibition*, 1912; Albright Art Gallery, Buffalo, 1913, and 1916 (National Sculpture Society).

PURCHASE, ROGERS FUND, 1912.

A Torso   27.21.4

A nude woman seated with legs crossed.

Bronze, height 13¼ in. Signed: Evelyn Beatrice Longman. Dated 1911. Founder's mark: Roman Bronze Works N.Y.

REPLICA: Private collection, New York.

EXHIBITED: National Sculpture Society, Buffalo (Albright Art Gallery), 1916.

GIFT OF EDWARD D. ADAMS, 1927.

Henry Bacon   24.153

Head of Henry Bacon (1866–1924), American architect, designer of the Lincoln Memorial in Washington and many other monuments designed in collaboration with Daniel Chester French.

Bronze, height 17 in. Signed: Evelyn Beatrice Longman, Sculptor. Dated 1918. Inscribed: Henry Bacon. Founder's mark: Roman Bronze Works N.Y.

REPLICA: Private collection, New York (?).

EXHIBITED: National Academy of Design, New York, 1918; Pennsylvania Academy of the Fine Arts, Philadelphia, 1919; Art Institute of Chicago, 1919.

GIFT OF MRS. EVELYN B. LONGMAN BATCHELDER, 1924.

Mr. and Mrs. Robert W. de Forest   46.118

This marble medallion was made in 1922, "as a tribute of respect and affection," from her design for a bronze medal commemorating the golden wedding anniversary of Mr. and Mrs. de Forest. Robert W. de Forest (1848–1931) was President of the Board of Trustees of the Museum from 1913 to 1931, having been made a Trustee in 1889, Secretary of the Board of Trustees in 1904, and a Vice-President of the Board in 1909. He was elected a Benefactor of the Museum in 1920, and his wife Emily Johnston de Forest, daughter of John Taylor Johnston, Founder and first President of the Museum, was also a Benefactor. Mr. and Mrs. de Forest gave the American Wing to the Museum in 1924.

Marble, diameter 10½ in. (set in wooden frame). Signed: E B L (monogram). Inscribed: Robert Weeks de Forest Emily Johnston de Forest 1872 1922.

REPLICAS: Four hundred medals were struck and distributed at the reception celebrating the golden wedding anniversary of Mr. and Mrs. de Forest. A few bronze medallions were struck for distribution to members of the family.

EX COLL. Mr. and Mrs. Robert W. de Forest, New York.

GIFT OF JOHNSTON DE FOREST, 1946.

Charles Keck
1875–1951

BORN and died in New York. After studying at the Art Students League and the National Academy of Design, Keck was a student of Philip Martiny and Saint-Gaudens from 1893 to 1898. He received a Rinehart scholarship and continued his studies at the American Academy in Rome from 1900 to 1904, with trips to Florence, Paris, and Greece. When he returned, he opened a studio in New York.

52.152

In 1909 he made a statue of Mohammed or The Genius of Islam for the façade of the Brooklyn Museum. His Victory in Montclair, New Jersey, was awarded a Medal of Honor by the Architectural League in 1926. The Masonic order gave him the Grand Medal for Distinguished Achievement for his statue of the World War chaplain Father Duffy, in Times Square, New York.

Keck was a member of the National Sculpture Society, the Architectural League of New York, the National Academy of Design, and the American Numismatic Society.

Elihu Vedder   52.152

Bust of Elihu Vedder (1836–1923), American painter and illustrator.

Bronze, height 20¼ in. Inscribed: Rome.

EXHIBITED: National Academy of Design, New York, 1947.

GIFT OF MRS. CHARLES KECK, 1952.

Skating Girl   48.117

A statuette made in 1948.

Bronze, height 16 in. Signed: C. Keck. Copy-

righted; founder's mark: Roman Bronze Works N.Y.

REPLICAS: According to the sculptor five bronze replicas were made. The other four are in private collections in New York.

REFERENCE: *Ice Skating News* (New York), 1 (1949):3, ill.

GIFT OF DAVID T. LAYMAN, JR., 1948.

Other Works

27.208. Medal commemorating the founding of the government of the state of New York, with head of George Clinton. 1927. Bronze, diameter 2⁷⁄₁₆ in. Gift of Alphonso T. Clearwater, 1927.

16.128. Portrait medal of Lewis Stephen Pilcher. Reverse inscribed: To commemorate fifty years of practice surgeon author editor patriot 1916. Silver, diameter 2¼ in. Gift of Lewis S. Pilcher, 1916.

Carl Milles

1875–1955

BORN at Lagga, Sweden; died in Lidingö, Sweden. Carl Milles's art training began in 1892, when he was apprenticed to a cabinetmaker in Stockholm. He also attended the Technical School there. From 1896 to 1904 he worked and exhibited in Paris, where at one time he assisted in Rodin's studio. Just after his marriage to Olga Granner in 1904, he became seriously ill from a lung inflammation caused by inhaling stone dust, an illness that continued to plague him for the rest of his life. His health prevented him from returning to Sweden until 1908, at which time he purchased the property now known as "Millesgarten" in the suburb Lidingö, overlooking Stockholm.

In 1920 he accepted a professorship at the Royal Academy in Stockholm, but the academic life hampered his independent spirit, and he returned to his studio in Lidingö. In

1931 he was asked to become head of the sculpture department at the Cranbrook Academy of Art in Michigan, and he moved to the United States. Because of his continuing residence in the United States, he placed Millesgarten in the hands of a private institution, which kept it open to the public. In 1945 he became an American citizen. From 1950 to 1955 Milles spent the winter months working in Rome at the invitation of the American Academy. He died at his home in Lidingö.

Head of Orpheus   40.149

Orpheus was the Greek god of music. This is a replica of the head of the central figure in the Orpheus Fountain in Stockholm. The competition for the fountain was held in 1926, and the commission was awarded to Milles in 1930. The final models were completed in 1934, and the fountain erected in 1936.

Cast iron, height 28½ in. Signed: Carl Milles. Founder's mark: Herman Bergman Fud. Sweden.

REPLICAS: According to the sculptor three casts of the head were made, one in bronze and two in iron.

40.149

REFERENCES: M. Rogers, *Carl Milles* (1940); P. Remington, *Met. Mus. Bull.*, old series 36 (1941); 58, ill. cover.

EXHIBITED: Philadelphia Museum of Art, 1940; American Academy of Arts and Letters, New York, 1943; National Institute of Arts and Letters, New York, 1947.

PURCHASE, ROGERS FUND, 1940.

Fountain of Aganippe   54.198.1–16

The fountain was commissioned in 1949 specially for the Metropolitan Museum and, appropriately, depicts the mythological fountain out of which flowed the waters of artistic inspiration. The scene represented is described in the artist's own words: "Of the eight fountain figures round and in the pool, five of these represent the arts—men who just have been drinking the holy water from the Goddess Aganippe's well. Famous water helping the musical artists as well as all artists to get the right spirit to work and create. Here we see them rushing home filled with enthusiasm— each one with his new ideas forcing them to hurry. Each artist carries his symbol with him: The Poete, the blue bird. The Architect his new formed column. The Musician his old interesting instrument. The Painter—here represented by Eugene Delacroix—his Flowers.

"The Sculptor is reaching for his gift from the Gods—as the Painter and the Musician have not yet grasped their symbols. These gifts from their Gods are just coming. These Artists *feel* them and grasp for them.

"Behind these running artists are: The Goddess Aganippe waving good wishes to the artists, and in the same time playing with a fish below in the water.

"A centaur has dressed up to mirroring himself in the water—on the other side is a faune taking musical lessons from a bird."
1. The poet carrying a bluebird, height 114 in.
2. Aganippe, height 37 in.
3. The architect carrying his column, height 108 in.
4. The musician carrying his instrument, height 105 in.

5. The painter, representing Eugène Delacroix, carrying flowers, height 117 in.
6. The sculptor holding a horse with rider, height 120 in.
7. Centaur, height 42 in.
8. Faun, height 55½ in.
9–11. Dolphins, height 24 in.
12. Leaping fish, height 11 in.
13. Fountainhead: fish head, height 5½ in. (not installed).
14. Fountainhead: boar, height 6⅛ in.
15. Fountainhead: wolf, height 5⅝ in.
16. Fountainhead: horse, height 7⅝ in.

54.198.3

54.198.2

54.198.5

Bronze (cast by Bearzi, Florence).

REPLICAS: Millesgarten, Lidingö, Sweden (Nos. 1, 2, 4, 6, and two fish).

REFERENCE: Francis Henry Taylor, "Aganippe: The Fountain of the Muses," *Met. Mus. Bull.*, new series 14 (1956):109.

PURCHASE, ROGERS FUND, 1954.

54.198.4

54.198.7

54.198.6

54.198.8

Anna Vaughn Hyatt Huntington

1876–

Mrs. Archer M. Huntington. Born in Cambridge, Massachusetts. Anna Hyatt studied sculpture in Boston with Henry Hudson Kitson and in New York, at the Art Students League, with Hermon MacNeil and Gutzon Borglum.

Winter Noon   06.302

Two dray horses, also called Winter, Resting, and Winter Group, made about 1902.

Bronze, height 7½ in. Signed: Anna V. Hyatt. Copyrighted; founder's mark: Roman Bronze Works N.Y. No. 7.

REPLICAS: Judging from the founder's mark at least seven examples were cast in bronze.

REFERENCE: *Catalogue of Sculpture* (Metropolitan Museum, 1908).

EXHIBITED: Society of American Artists, New York, 1903; Louisiana Purchase Exposition, St. Louis, 1904; Pennsylvania Academy of the Fine Arts, Philadelphia, 1904; Art Institute of Chicago, 1910; Panama Pacific Exposition, San Francisco, 1915; National Sculpture Society, Buffalo (Albright Art Gallery), 1916; Detroit Institute of Arts, 1916.

PURCHASE, ROGERS FUND, 1906.

Tigers Watching   06.303

Two tigers.

Bronze, height 7 in. Signed: Anna V. Hyatt. Copyrighted; founder's mark: Roman Bronze Works N.Y. No. 5.

REPLICAS: Judging from the founder's mark at least five examples were cast in bronze.

REFERENCE: *Catalogue of Sculpture* (Metropolitan Museum, 1908).

EXHIBITED: Pennsylvania Academy of the Fine Arts, Philadelphia, 1906; Art Institute of Chicago, 1910; Panama Pacific Exposition, San Francisco, 1915.

PURCHASE, ROGERS FUND, 1906.

Goats Fighting   12.51

A statuette of two goats, also called Goats Butting.

Bronze, height 10¼ in. Signed: Anna V. Hyatt. Copyrighted; founder's mark: Roman Bronze Works N.Y.

REPLICA: Detroit Institute of Arts.

EXHIBITED: Society of American Artists, New York, 1905; Pennsylvania Academy of the Fine Arts, Philadelphia, 1906; Detroit Institute of Arts, 1916.

PURCHASE, ROGERS FUND, 1912.

12.51

Reaching Jaguar   26.85.1

A companion piece to the following entry, Jaguar. The original model was made in 1906.

Bronze, height 45 in. Copyrighted; founder's mark: Jno. Williams Inc. N.Y. 1926.

REPLICAS: Brookgreen Gardens, South Carolina (bronze); Zoological Park, New York (stone); Mariners Museum Park, Newport News, Virginia (marble); Musée du Luxembourg, Paris (stone variant); private collection, Davenport, Iowa (bronze).

REFERENCE: B. G. Proske, *Brookgreen Gardens, Sculpture* (1943).

EXHIBITED: Paris, Salon of 1908 (plaster); Women's Art Club, New York; Panama Pacific Exposition, San Francisco, 1915; National Sculpture Society, Buffalo (Albright Art Gallery), 1916; Metropolitan Museum, 1918 (plaster).

GIFT OF ARCHER M. HUNTINGTON, 1926.

Jaguar   26.85.2

A companion piece to the preceding entry, Reaching Jaguar. The original model was made in 1906.

Bronze, height 28½ in. Signed: Anna V. Hyatt. Copyrighted; founder's mark: Jno Williams Inc 1926.

REPLICAS: Brookgreen Gardens, South Carolina (bronze); Zoological Gardens, New York (stone); Mariners Museum Park, Newport News, Virginia (marble); private collection, Davenport, Iowa (bronze).

REFERENCE: B. G. Proske, *Brookgreen Gardens, Sculpture* (1943).

GIFT OF ARCHER M. HUNTINGTON, 1926.

Other Works

16.24.1. Jetton commemorating the unveiling of a statue of Joan of Arc. Bronze, 1¾ x 1⅛ in. Gift of the Joan of Arc Committee, 1916.

43.65.1. Medal of African animals. 1943. Bronze, diameter 2⅞ in. Gift of the Society of Medalists, 1943.

Helen Farnsworth Mears

1876–1916

BORN in Oshkosh, Wisconsin; died in New York. In a letter sent to the Museum in 1905, Helen Mears says that she studied with Au-

26.85.1

gustus Saint-Gaudens in New York, and under Puech, Merson, Charpentier, and Collin in Paris. She exhibited at the Paris Salon of 1897, and won a prize at the World's Fair in Chicago in 1893 for a statue representing the state of Wisconsin, and a Silver Medal for a bas-relief, The Fountain of Life, at the Louisiana Purchase Exposition in St. Louis in 1904. The Society of the Children of the American Revolution gave her a commission for a bust of General George Rogers Clark, and she executed a nine-foot statue in marble, The Genius of Wisconsin, as a commission from that state. Helen Mears was a favorite pupil of Augustus Saint-Gaudens, and she made a bronze portrait relief of him. After her death the contents of her studio were presented to the Milwaukee Art Gallery.

Edward Alexander MacDowell

09.147

Mary Mears, the sister of the sculptor, who was present when this relief of MacDowell (1861–1908), American musician, composer,

09.147

and teacher, was being modeled, wrote of it, "The text placed on the bas-relief, 'Night has fallen on a day of deeds,' is from one of his own poems and the third movement of the Sonata Tragica. . . . was selected by the composer himself to be inscribed on this last portrait."

Bronze, height 33¼ in., width 39⅞ in. (mounted on a flat wood frame). Inscribed: (at top) Edward Alexander MacDowell composer musician and poet aetatis XLV Night has fallen on a day of deeds; (on scroll superimposed on laurel wreath) Sonata Tragica III [with the musical notation of the opening bars]; (at lower left) modelled from life by Helen Farnsworth Mears MDCCCCVI. Copyrighted.

REPLICAS: Edward MacDowell Association, Inc., New York; Columbia University, New York.

REFERENCE: Mary Mears, "The Work and Home of Edward MacDowell, Musician," *The Craftsman*, 16 (1909):416, ill. frontis.

EXHIBITED: National Sculpture Society, Baltimore, 1908, and Buffalo (Albright Art Gallery), 1916; Pennsylvania Academy of the Fine Arts, Philadelphia, 1908, 1912.

GIFT OF MISS ALICE G. CHAPMAN, 1909.

Henry Clews, Jr.

1876–1937

BORN in New York City; died in France. Clews, the son of the banker Henry Clews, was educated in private schools and at Amherst College and Columbia University; he also studied at the universities of Lausanne and Hanover. After a brief period in the family banking firm he turned his attention to painting and sculpture, working independently in New York and in Paris. From 1914 on, except for occasional visits to the United States, he lived in France, settling near Cannes in 1918. Between 1903 and 1914 seven exhibitions of his paintings and sculpture were held in New York. A memorial exhibition of his sculpture was held in this Museum in 1939.

39.118.1

Many of his sculptures are in a grotesque decorative style and were designed as ornaments for his château at La Napoule.

Frederick Delius   39.118.1

Portrait of the English composer Delius (1862–1934), in the form of a mask, modeled in 1916 and 1917.

Bronze (cast by Valsuani), height 15¾ in. Signed: Clews. Dated: Paris 1936.

REPLICAS: La Napoule Art Foundation, Henry Clews Memorial; private collection, Cannes, 1939; Delius Museum, Bradford, England.

REFERENCES: *Sculpture by Henry Clews Jr.* (exhibition cat., Metropolitan Museum, 1939); P. Remington, *Met. Mus. Bull.*, old series 35 (1940):44.

EXHIBITED: Metropolitan Museum, 1939.

GIFT OF MRS. HENRY CLEWS, JR., 1939.

The Mayor of Mandelieu   39.118.2

A bust of Laurent Gandolphe, the mayor of a small French town.

Bronze, height 34¾ in. Signed: Clews. Dated: La Napoule 1934. Founder's mark: C. Valsuani cire perdue.

REPLICA: La Napoule Art Foundation, Henry Clews Memorial.

REFERENCES: *Sculpture by Henry Clews Jr.* (exhibition cat., Metropolitan Museum, 1939); P. Remington, *Met. Mus. Bull.*, old series 35 (1940):44.

EXHIBITED: Metropolitan Museum, 1939.

GIFT OF MRS. HENRY CLEWS, JR., 1939.

James Earle Fraser
1876–1953

BORN in Winona, Minnesota; died in Westport, Connecticut. At eighteen, Fraser entered the studio of Richard Bock in Chicago,

29.95

at the same time attending drawing classes at the Chicago Art Institute. He left there to study under Falguière at the École des Beaux-Arts in Paris. Saint-Gaudens was sufficiently impressed with the young sculptor to employ him as an assistant in his studio. Fraser worked there until 1902, when he established his own studio in New York City. From 1906 to 1911 he taught at the Art Students League. He served as vice-president of the National Institute of Arts and Letters from 1925 to 1929 and as president of the National Sculpture Society from 1925 to 1926. Perhaps his most famous piece of sculpture is The End of the Trail, in Waupun, Wisconsin. He also designed the United States buffalo nickel.

Elihu Root   29.95

Bust of Elihu Root (1845–1937), American lawyer and statesman, who was a Trustee and Vice-President of this Museum from 1900 to 1931.

Bronze, height 17¾ in. Signed: J. E. Fraser. Dated 1926. Copyrighted; founder's mark: Kunst-F'dry N.Y.

REPLICAS: Chatham House, London; Carnegie Corporation, New York; National Art Collection, Smithsonian Institution, Washington; Carnegie Endowment for International Peace, Washington; Carnegie Institution, Washington; Army War College, Washington (marble); Council on Foreign Relations, New York; New York State Bar Association, New York; Carnegie Institute, Pittsburgh.

GIFT OF THE CARNEGIE CORPORATION, 1929.

Head of a Young Artist 33.93

Portrait head of a man, modeled in 1921 and 1922 and cut in stone in 1933.

Marble, height 16½ in. Signed: J. Fraser.

REFERENCE: P. Remington, *Met. Mus. Bull.*, old series 28 (1933):177.

PURCHASE, ROGERS FUND, 1933.

Other Works

09.114. Portrait medal of Augustus Saint-Gaudens, medal of honor of the Pan American Exposition. 1901. Bronze, diameter 3⁹⁄₁₆ in. Gift of Mr. and Mrs. Frederick S. Wait, 1909.

17.41.1. Henry Elias Howland memorial medal, Yale University. Bronze, diameter 2⅞ in. Gift of Charles P. Howland, 1917.

53.12.1. Medal inscribed: New frontiers. 1952. Bronze, diameter 2⅞ in. Gift of the Society of Medalists, 1953.

Herbert Willis Clark, Jr.
1877–1920

BORN in Providence, Rhode Island. Clark was trained as a sculptor at the Rhode Island School of Design and specialized in making statuettes of horses. He was employed as a designer of small decorative bronzes by the Gorham Company.

Saddle Horse 20.34

Bronze, height 16¼ in. Inscribed: Copyright 1911 by Herbert W. Clark Jr. New York. Founder's mark: Gorham Co. Founders Q. I. C.

GIFT OF HERBERT WILLIS CLARK, JR., 1920.

Edgar Walter
1877–1938

BORN in San Francisco. Walter studied sculpture under Douglas Tilden at the Mark Hopkins Art Institute in San Francisco and with Chopin and Perrin in Paris. He exhibited sculpture at the Paris Salon in 1898 and 1899, 1901 through 1903, and 1905 and 1906.

33.93

07.112

Primitive Man 07.112

A young man lifting a bear cub by the scruff of the neck, made about 1902.

Bronze, height 31 in. Signed: E. Walter Copyrighted.

REPLICAS: Private collection, San Francisco; Toledo Museum of Art. A small-size bronze was formerly in the Museum's collection.

REFERENCES: *Met. Mus. Bull.*, old series 2 (1907):87; *Catalogue of Sculpture* (Metropolitan Museum, 1908).

EXHIBITED: Paris, Salon, 1903 (plaster), 1905 (bronze).

GIFT OF ISAAC N. SELIGMAN, 1907.

Gertrude Vanderbilt Whitney

1877–1942

BORN and died in New York City. Gertrude Vanderbilt Whitney was the daughter of Cornelius and Alice Claypoole (Gwynne) Vanderbilt. She married Harry Payne Whitney in

1896. Her training in sculpture was under Hendrick C. Andersen and James Earle Fraser and at the Art Students League in New York; later she was a pupil of Andrew O'Connor and Rodin in Paris. She was given a number of commissions for monuments; among the best known of these are her equestrian statue of Buffalo Bill at Cody, Wyoming, the St. Nazaire Monument in France, the Titanic Memorial in Washington, and the Columbus Monument at the port of Palos, Spain. Her work was awarded Honorable Mention at the Paris Salon in 1913, and she was given many honors at other exhibitions. Mrs. Whitney was the founder of the Whitney Museum of American Art.

Head of a Spanish Peasant 16.84

A portrait of a man.

Bronze, height 21¼ in. Signed: G. Whitney. Dated 1911.

16.84

REPLICAS: Detroit Institute of Arts (as Italian Peasant). Six bronze casts are believed to have been made.

REFERENCE: *Gertrude Vanderbilt Whitney Memorial Exhibition Catalogue* (Whitney Museum of American Art, 1943).

EXHIBITED: Detroit Institute of Arts, 1918; Whitney Museum of American Art, New York, 1943.

PURCHASE, ROGERS FUND, 1916.

A Caryatid   22.81

A standing nude man, a study for one of the caryatids supporting the basin of a fountain originally designed for use in the Arlington Hotel in Washington.

Bronze, height 22⅝ in. Signed: Gertrude V. Whitney. Dated 1913. Copyrighted; founder's mark: C. Valsuani Cire Perdue.

REPLICAS: Brookgreen Gardens, South Carolina. Six bronze casts are believed to have been made. A marble replica of the whole fountain is at McGill University, Montreal.

REFERENCES: *New York Sun* (Nov. 5, 1916); *Arts and Decoration*, 6 (1916):342; B. G. Proske, *Brookgreen Gardens, Sculpture* (1943); *Gertrude Vanderbilt Whitney Memorial Exhibition Catalogue* (Whitney Museum of American Art, 1943).

EXHIBITED: Paris, Salon of 1913 (marble fountain), Honorable Mention; Detroit Institute of Arts, 1918; Knoedler Galleries, New York, 1936.

ANONYMOUS GIFT, 1922.

Stuart Benson

1877–1949

BORN in Detroit, Michigan; died at sea. After attending the Detroit High School and the University of Michigan, Benson studied art at the Joseph Gies School of Art in Detroit.

He left there to become art editor of *Collier's Magazine* in New York, where he later became art director of the A. W. Erickson Advertising Agency. His plans to settle in France and devote his life to sculpture were interrupted by the first World War. He was later created Chevalier of the Legion of Honor by the French government and was awarded the Croix de Guerre and the Croix de l'Étoile Noire. After the war he returned to New York, once again as art director of *Collier's Magazine*. At this time he wrote several short stories and plays. He finally embarked for France, where he continued to spend his summers in his studio at Colle-sur-Loup in the Maritime Alps. He was a member of the National Sculpture Society.

The Woman Who Came from Siberia   39.36

Portrait head, made in 1938.

Bronze, height 18 in. Signed: S. B. (monogram). Founder's mark: Cire Perdue A. Valsuani.

REFERENCE: F. Dennis, *Met. Mus. Bull.*, old series 34 (1939):159.

EXHIBITED: Ferargil Gallery, New York, 1938.

ANONYMOUS GIFT, 1939.

Albert Laessle

1877–1954

BORN in Philadelphia; died in Miami, Florida. Laessle studied at the Pennsylvania Academy of the Fine Arts under Thomas Anshutz and Charles Grafly. He specialized in animal sculpture but also executed a number of portrait busts and medals. From 1904 to 1907 he studied in Paris, where he received some instruction from Michael Beguine. He taught at the Pennsylvania Academy of the Fine Arts from 1921 to 1939. During the course of his career he was awarded a number of honors, medals, and prizes, and he became a member of the National Sculpture Society, the National Academy of Design, and the National Institute of Arts and Letters. Several of his animal sculptures and his large monument to General Pennypacker ornament the parks and squares of his native city.

Turning Turtle   17.63

A capsized turtle turning himself over.

Bronze, height 8 in. Signed: Albert Laessle. Dated: Paris, 1905. Founder's mark: Roman Bronze Works N.Y.

REPLICA: Brookgreen Gardens, South Carolina.

REFERENCE: B. G. Proske, *Brookgreen Gardens, Sculpture* (1943).

EXHIBITED: Paris, Salon of 1907; Pennsylvania Academy of the Fine Arts, Philadelphia, 1908; National Academy of Design, New York, 1908; Panama Pacific Exposition, San Francisco, 1915; National Sculpture Society, Buffalo (Albright Art Gallery), 1916; Sesqui-Centennial Exposition, Philadelphia, 1926.

PURCHASE, ROGERS FUND, 1917.

Victory   20.19

An eagle.

Bronze, height 18½ in. Signed: Albert Laessle. Dated: Germantown, Philadelphia, 1918. Copyrighted; founder's mark: Roman Bronze Works N.Y.

REPLICA: Formerly collection of the sculptor, Philadelphia (bronze).

EXHIBITED: Pennsylvania Academy of the Fine Arts, Philadelphia, 1919; Art Institute of Chicago, 1919; Sesqui-Centennial Exposition, Philadelphia, 1926; Brooklyn Museum, New York, 1930.

PURCHASE, AMELIA B. LAZARUS FUND, 1920.

Other Works

34.139.1. Medal showing an ear of corn and a turkey. Inscribed: Abundance; (reverse) America. 1934. Bronze, diameter 2⅞ in. Gift of the Society of Medalists, 1934.

Mahonri Young

1877–1957

BORN in Salt Lake City, Utah; died in Norwalk, Connecticut. Young studied drawing under James T. Harwood in Salt Lake City and in 1899 went to the Art Students League in New York. In 1901 he went to Paris to study at the Académie Julian. A trip to Italy brought about a change of interest from drawing and painting to sculpture, although he continued to attend occasional sketching classes at the Académie Delécluse in Paris. His special interest in the cowboys, animals, and Indians of the West was stimulated by a trip to Arizona in 1912.

Among his awards are the Barnett Prize of the National Academy of Design in 1911, a Silver Medal at the Panama Pacific Exposition in 1915, and the First Prize for Sculpture at the Olympic Games in 1932. He was a member of the National Sculpture Society, the National Academy of Design, the Society of American Etchers, and the National Institute of Arts and Letters.

Stevedore   14.27

This statuette of a worker carrying a large sack on his shoulders was made in 1904.

Bronze, height 16½ in. Signed: M. M. Young. Founder's mark: Roman Bronze Works N.Y.

REPLICAS: According to the sculptor six bronze casts were made.

REFERENCE: *Mahonri M. Young, Retrospective Exhibition* (Addison Gallery of American Art, 1940).

EXHIBITED: National Sculpture Society, New York, 1923; Baltimore Museum of Art, 1923; Addison Gallery of American Art, Andover, Massachusetts, 1940.

PURCHASE, ROGERS FUND, 1914.

Man with a Pick   18.107

Made between 1912 and 1917.

Bronze, height 28½ in. Signed: M. Young. Founder's mark: Roman Bronze Works N.Y.

REPLICAS: According to the sculptor two bronzes were cast.

REFERENCE: *Mahonri M. Young, Retrospective Exhibition* (Addison Gallery of American Art, 1940).

108.17

Other Works

35.135. Medal commemorating the Twelfth Night celebration of the Century Association. 1933. Bronze, diameter 2⅜ in. Rogers Fund, 1935.

45.31.1. Medal inscribed: Riggers; (reverse) Riveters. 1945. Bronze, diameter 2¹³⁄₁₆ in. Gift of the Society of Medalists, 1945.

Maurice Sterne

1877–1957

BORN in Libau, Russia; died in Mt. Kisco, New York. Sterne came to the United States in 1889 and trained in both painting and sculpture at the National Academy of Design and other art schools in New York. He also studied under Thomas Eakins. In 1904, he traveled to France, Italy, Greece, and the Orient. He was made an associate member of the National Academy in 1935 and a member of the National Institute of Arts and Letters in 1938. Sterne was better known for his work as a painter, etcher, and draftsman.

The Bomb-Thrower   22.97

A portrait head sometimes called Pasquale. According to the sculptor this is the first of three variants on an original made in Rome in 1910.

Bronze, height 12 ¼ in.

REPLICAS: Private collection, New York (original version); private collection, New York (second variant); Worcester Art Museum, Massachusetts (third variant).

REFERENCES: M. Birnbaum, *International Studio*, 46 (1912): vi, xiii, ill; *Maurice Sterne Retrospective Exhibition* (Museum of Modern Art, 1933).

22.97

Herbert Haseltine

1877–1962

BORN in Rome; died in Paris. Haseltine, the son of the American landscape painter William Stanley Haseltine, was encouraged by his family in his desire to paint and draw. He was educated in Italy and in the United States, graduating from Harvard College in 1899. He went to Munich to study art at the Royal Academy, and he also studied in Rome and at the Académie Julian in Paris. About 1905 he became a pupil of Aimé Morot, who suggested that he try his hand at sculpture. One of his first efforts at modeling—a group of polo players—was exhibited at the Salon in Paris in 1906 and was awarded Honorable Mention. From this time forward his principal interest was in modeling animals, especially thoroughbred horses. His career in sculpture was interrupted by the first World War when he served as a special assistant to the United States Ambassador to France and as a Captain of Engineers. At the end of the war he became interested in Egyptian sculpture. This had a profound effect upon his style, first visible in the group of twenty British champion animals exhibited in Paris in 1925. Among his larger statues are the equestrian George Washington placed before the National Cathedral in Washington, the statue of the famous race horse Man o' War in Lexington, Kentucky, the equestrian monument to an Indian Rajah in Nawanagar, and the monument to Field Marshal Sir John Greer Dill of the British Army, now in Arlington Cemetery.

Percheron Stallion: Ruhm   26.160.1

One of a group of portraits of British champion animals. Ruhm's record is as follows: Foaled 1917. Sire: Lagor. Dam: Mazurka. Bred by Monsieur Chopin of La Bigottière, Bellême, Mortagne, France, and the property of Mrs. Robert Emmet, The Greyling Stud, Moreton Morrell, Warwickshire. First at Mortagne, 1919. First and Champion at the shows of the Royal Agricultural Society of England, 1921, 1922, and 1923. First and Champion, Norwich Stallion Show, 1922, 1923.

Partly gilt bronze set with coral and onyx, height 28 in. Signed: Haseltine. Dated MCMXXV. Founder's mark: Alexis Rudier Fondeur. Paris.

REPLICAS: Private collection, Moreton Morrell, Warwickshire, England (bronze); Field Museum, Chicago (marble); Addison Gallery, Andover, Massachusetts (gilt bronze); private collection, Dayton, Ohio; London art market, 1930.

REFERENCES: *Herbert Haseltine, Exhibition of Sculpture* (Knoedler Galleries, London, 1930); *Sculptures by Herbert Haseltine* (Field Museum, Chicago, 1934); *Herbert Haseltine (American Sculptors Series*, no. 7, c. 1948).

EXHIBITED: Galerie Georges Petit, Paris, 1925; Knoedler Galleries, London, 1925, 1930; Knoedler Galleries, New York, 1934; Fogg Art Museum, Cambridge, Massachusetts, 1934; Berkshire Museum, Pittsfield, Massachusetts.

GIFT OF MRS. GEORGE BLUMENTHAL, 1926.

Percheron Mare and Foal: Messaline
26.160.2

One of a group of British champion animals, companion piece to the preceding entry. Messaline's record is as follows: Foaled 1912. Sire: Douvreur-ex-Couvreur. Dam: Paquerette. Bred in France, and the property of Mrs. Robert Emmet, The Greyling Stud, Moreton Morrell, Warwickshire. First, Mortagne Show, 1917, 1918, 1919. First, show of the Royal Counties Agricultural Society, 1920. First, and Group Prize, at the show of the Norfolk Agricultural Society, 1920. First at the show of the Royal Agricultural Society of England, 1920.

Bronze set with onyx, height 21¾ in. Signed: Haseltine. Dated MCMXXV. Founder's mark: Alexis Rudier Fondeur Paris.

REPLICAS: Private collection, Moreton Morrell, Warwickshire, England; Field Museum, Chicago (marble); Addison Gallery, Andover, Massachusetts (gilt bronze); Rhode Island School of Design, Providence (formerly in collection of Sir William Orpen) (stone); private collection, Dayton, Ohio.

REFERENCES: See preceding entry.

EXHIBITED: See preceding entry.

GIFT OF MRS. GEORGE BLUMENTHAL, 1926.

Suffolk Punch Stallion: Sudbourne Premier   50.145.39

One of a group of portraits of British champion animals. Sudbourne Premier's record is as follows: Foaled 1919. Sire: Sudbourne Beau Brocade. Dam: Sudbourne Moonlight. Bred

26.160.2

by the Right Honorable Lord Manton, and the property of Percy C. Vestey of Easton Park, Wickham Market, Suffolk. First and Champion at the shows of the Royal Agricultural Society of England, 1921, 1922.

Bronze, height 12 in. Dated MCMXXV Paris.

REPLICAS: Musée du Luxembourg, Paris; Field Museum, Chicago; Tate Gallery, London; California Palace of the Legion of Honor, San Francisco; Eton College Art Museum, England; Pennsylvania Academy of the Fine Arts, Philadelphia.

REFERENCES: *Herbert Haseltine, Exhibition of Sculpture* (Knoedler Galleries, London, 1930); *Herbert Haseltine, Exhibition of Sculpture* (Knoedler Galleries, New York, 1934); *Sculptures by Herbert Haseltine* (Field Museum, Chicago, 1934); *Herbert Haseltine (American Sculptors Series*, no. 7, c. 1948).

EXHIBITED: Galerie Georges Petit, Paris, 1925; Knoedler Galleries, London, 1925, 1930; Knoedler Galleries, New York, 1934; Fogg Art Museum, Cambridge, Massachusetts, 1934.

BEQUEST OF MARY STILLMAN HARKNESS, 1950.

Lee Lawrie
1877–1963

BORN in Rixford, Germany; died in Easton, Maryland. Lawrie was brought to the United States as an infant. Between 1894 and 1906 he was employed in many sculptors' studios. He was known principally as an architectural sculptor.

Head of a Woman   26.19.2

A miniature portrait bust made at the request of Ralph Adams Cram to be used as the head of a statue of the Madonna for the Cathedral of St. John the Divine. The statue was never completed.

Marble, height 10¼ in. Signed: Lee Lawrie. Dated MCMXI. Inscribed: Hannah Thomas Slade 1825–1893.

REPLICA: A life-size replica is supposed to have been made but is unlocated.

GIFT OF MRS. CLINTON OGILVIE, 1926.

Other Works

33.152.9. Medal inscribed: Whatsoever a man soweth; (reverse) That shall he also reap. 1932. Bronze, diameter 2⅞ in. Gift of the Society of Medalists, 1933.

Abastenia St. Leger Eberle

1878–1942

BORN in Webster City, Iowa; died in New York. In 1899 Abastenia Eberle's interest in clay modeling brought her to the Art Students League in New York, where she studied with George Grey Barnard, Gutzon Borglum, and Kenyon Cox. For a time she worked in collaboration with Anna Vaughn Hyatt. She went to Italy in 1907 for a year and in 1913 was in Paris. In 1914 she opened a studio in the slums of New York, and most of her work from that time on was strongly influenced by the study of the people, especially the children, who lived there. Most of her work was done before 1919, when serious illness interrupted her career. Her interest in social subjects and the life of the New York streets relates her to the so-called "Ashcan School" of painters, who were in revolt against the "pretty" subjects favored by the conservative painters of an older generation.

Girl with Roller Skate   09.57

Also called Girl Skating, Roller Skater, and Roller Skating.

Bronze, height 13⅛ in. Signed: A. St. L. Eberle. Dated 1906.

REPLICAS: Whitney Museum of American Art, New York; Rhode Island School of Design, Providence. According to the sculptor, about eight bronze casts were made.

EXHIBITED: National Academy of Design, New York, *Winter Exhibition*, 1906, and *Annual Exhibition*, 1907; Pennsylvania Academy of the Fine Arts, Philadelphia, 1907, 1908; National Sculpture Society, Baltimore, 1908.

PURCHASE, ROGERS FUND, 1909.

Robert Ingersoll Aitken

1878–1949

BORN in San Francisco, California; died in New York. Aitken studied sculpture for a short time at the Mark Hopkins Art Institute in San Francisco under Douglas Tilden; this

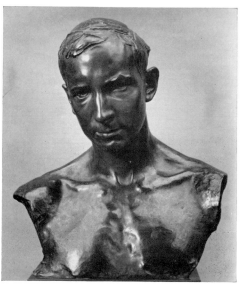

51.154

was his only training. While still a very young man he won two commissions for monuments in San Francisco. He worked in France from 1904 to 1907. On his return to the United States he settled in New York and became an instructor at the Art Students League. In 1915 Aitken executed a fountain for the Panama Pacific Exposition in San Francisco. Among his larger works are the sculptures for the pediment of the United States Supreme Court building in Washington. His work shows the influence of Michelangelo and Rodin. Aitken received many honors, he was president of the National Sculpture Society and a vice-president of the National Institute of Arts and Letters.

George Bellows   51.154

This bust of George Bellows (1882–1925), American painter and illustrator, was cast for the Museum in 1951 from the original plaster.

Bronze (cast by the Roman Bronze Works), height 20½ in. Signed: R. I. Aitken.

REPLICA: Columbus Gallery of Fine Arts, Ohio.

PURCHASE, FRANCIS LATHROP BEQUEST FUND, 1951.

Rudulph Evans
1878–1959

BORN and died in Washington, D. C. Evans studied at the School of the Corcoran Gallery of Art in Washington, the Art Students League in New York, and the Académie Julian and the École des Beaux-Arts in Paris under Falguière, Puech, and Rodin. He was awarded a Bronze Medal at the Paris Salon in 1914 and the Watrous Gold Medal at the National Academy of Design in 1919. He became a member of the National Institute of Arts and Letters in 1926 and a member of the National Academy of Design in 1929. In 1941 he won

the competition for a heroic bronze statue of Jefferson for the Jefferson Memorial in Washington. He was noted for his idealized portrait busts, some of which are in the Hall of Fame, New York University, and also for his statues and busts of children.

The Golden Hour   18.127

A letter from the sculptor states that this standing figure of a nude young girl was made in New York in 1913. It was cast in bronze in Paris in 1914 and in the same year received a medal at the Salon, from which it was purchased by the French government. The Metropolitan Museum's marble example was cut in Paris sometime between 1914 and 1918 by a Mr. Devaulx under the supervision of MacMonnies and was finished in New York by Evans.

A version of this figure without lower legs, arms, or head has been exhibited as Psyche Torso. The head also has been exhibited separately as a portrait of the sculptor's daughter.

Marble, height 66⅜ in. Signed: R. Evans.

REPLICAS: Private collection, New York (first bronze); Musée du Luxembourg, Paris (bronze).

REFERENCES: *International Studio*, 55 (1915): lxxxiv; C. H. Caffin, *Century Magazine*, 90 (1915):208; L. Taft, *History of American Sculpture* (1930).

EXHIBITED: Paris, Salon of 1914 (bronze).

GIFT OF FRANK A. VANDERLIP, 1918.

Margaret O'Laughlin Hoard
1879–1944

Mrs. Prescott D. Hoard. Born in Washington, Iowa; died in Mount Vernon, New York. Margaret Hoard studied art at Teachers College, Columbia University, and at the Art

Students League in New York. Besides her activities as a sculptor Mrs. Hoard designed wallpaper, gave lectures on the history of glassmaking, and was superintendent of the Public Lecture Bureau of New York City under the auspices of the Board of Education.

Eve   19.34

An article published in the Mount Vernon, New York, *Argus* in 1936 described this figure of a seated nude woman: "An exquisite figure of Eve meditating on the lamp of life overflowing beside her . . .; the figure seems to symbolize the futile groping of the human race toward an unattainable goal."

Marble, height 14 in. Signed: Margaret Hoard. Dated 1914.

REFERENCE: Mount Vernon, New York, *Argus* (July 30, 1936).

23.106.1

EXHIBITED: National Academy of Design, New York, *Winter Exhibition*, 1914; Panama Pacific Exposition, San Francisco, 1915; National Sculpture Society, Buffalo (Albright Art Gallery), 1916; Architectural League, 1917.

GIFT OF THEODORE STANFIELD, 1919.

Edward McCartan
1879–1947

BORN in Albany, New York; died in New York. McCartan studied sculpture with George Grey Barnard at Pratt Institute and at the Art Students League with Hermon MacNeil. In 1907 he went to Paris, where he studied at the École des Beaux-Arts under Injalbert for three years. At the National Academy Exhibition in 1912 he received the Barnett Prize for a fountain. The influence of Rodin is seen in his early works, for instance, The Kiss.

McCartan became known in architectural circles for his ornamental sculpture. He became associated with the Society of Beaux-Arts Architects, where he trained craftsmen in modeling and carving. He designed the pediment for the Department of Labor and Interstate Commerce Building in Washington. The Allied Artists of America awarded him the Gold Medal of Honor in 1933. He was president of the Concord Art Association, vice-president of the National Academy of Design, and a member of the National Sculpture Society and the National Institute of Arts and Letters.

Diana   23.106.1

Royal Cortissoz, writing of McCartan's work in general and of this figure, modeled in 1920, in particular, said: "He is a child of Houdon, say, simply in that it is natural to him to compose in terms of an animated mundane elegance and to stress in his figures the precious quality of line. The Diana is perhaps his outstanding triumph in this regard."

Bronze, height 24 in. Signed: E. McCartan. Dated 1923. Copyrighted; founder's mark: Roman Bronze Works N.Y.

REPLICAS: Private collection, Greenwich, Connecticut (life size); Brookgreen Gardens, South Carolina; Fogg Art Museum, Cambridge, Massachusetts; Canajoharie Art Gallery, Canajoharie, New York.

REFERENCES: R. Cortissoz, *Scribner's Magazine*, 83 (1928):236; B. G. Proske, *Brookgreen Gardens, Sculpture* (1943).

EXHIBITED: National Sculpture Society, New York, 1923; Art Institute of Chicago, 1923; Albright Art Gallery, Buffalo, 1924; Concord Art Association, Concord, Massachusetts, 1925, Medal of Honor.

PURCHASE, ROGERS FUND, 1923.

Helen Wills Moody   52.80

A portrait of the American champion tennis player.

Terra cotta, height 15½ in. Signed: E. McCartan. Dated 1936.

GIFT OF HENRY PARSONS, 1952.

Other Works

39.86.1. Medal inscribed: The old world; (reverse) The new world. 1939. Bronze, diameter 2⅞ in. Gift of the Society of Medalists, 1939.

John Gregory

1879–1958

BORN in London; died in New York. Gregory came to the United States from England at the age of fourteen. In 1900 he entered the Art Students League, studying sculpture under J. Massey Rhind, George Grey Barnard, and Hermon MacNeil. After three years he returned to London to pursue his studies for a year at Lambeth. The two years following were spent with Mercié in Paris at the École des Beaux-Arts, and in 1906 Gregory returned

to New York to work as assistant to MacNeil, Gutzon Borglum, and Herbert Adams. After becoming naturalized in 1912, he spent three years as a fellow at the American Academy in Rome. He was an academician of the National Academy of Design, a member of the National Institute of Arts and Letters, and honorary president of the National Sculpture Society in 1954.

Philomela   23.106.2

Philomela, who was transformed into a nightingale, is shown by Gregory as a kneeling nude woman with wings.

Bronze, height 14 in. Signed: John Gregory. Dated 1922. Inscribed: Philomela No. 11. Copyrighted; founder's mark: Roman Bronze Works N.Y.

REPLICAS: According to the sculptor eleven bronze replicas were made.

EXHIBITED: Architectural League, New York, 1921 (plaster), Medal of Honor; Fine Arts Building, New York, *Retrospective of American Art*, 1921; National Sculpture Society, New York, 1923; Art Institute of Chicago, 1923; Baltimore Museum of Art, 1923; Pennsylvania Academy of the Fine Arts, Philadelphia, 1924; Concord Art Association, Concord, Massachusetts, 1926, Medal of Honor.

PURCHASE, ROGERS FUND, 1923.

Other Works

39.150.1. Bethrothal medal. Inscribed: Ceres' blessing so is on you; (reverse) Scarcity and want shall shun you. 1939. Gold-plated bronze, diameter 2⅞ in. Gift of the Society of Medalists, 1939.

Albin Polasek

1879–1965

BORN in Frenstat, Moravia (now in Czechoslovakia). Polasek was trained as a wood-carver before coming to the United States in 1901.

He studied sculpture at the Pennsylvania Academy of the Fine Arts in Philadelphia under Charles Grafly and was later a Fellow of the American Academy in Rome. For many years he was an instructor in sculpture at the Chicago Art Institute.

Fantasy   14.79

Figure of a standing nude woman, made in Rome in 1913.

Bronze, height 20 in. Signed: A. Polasek.

REPLICAS: Private collection, Chicago (bronze). According to the sculptor only two bronze casts were made. Another work by the sculptor is a variation of this figure.

EXHIBITED: Architectural League, New York, 1914; Panama Pacific Exposition, San Francisco, 1915; National Sculpture Society, Buffalo (Albright Art Gallery), 1916; Brooklyn Museum, New York, 1930.

PURCHASE, ROGERS FUND, 1914.

Renée Prahar

1880-1963

BORN in New York. Renée Prahar studied sculpture at the École des Beaux-Arts in Paris under Injalbert and with Bourdelle.

Russian Dancer   18.106

A nude woman, made about 1915.

Bronze, height 18¼ in. Signed: Prahar. Founder's mark: B. Zoppo Foundry N Y.

EXHIBITED: National Academy of Design, New York, *Winter Exhibition*, 1915; Pennsylvania Academy of the Fine Arts, Philadelphia, 1916 (in both exhibitions as Dancer, same subject?).

GIFT OF ALFREDO SIDES, 1918.

Harriet Frishmuth

1880-

BORN in Philadelphia. Harriet Frishmuth studied at the Art Students League in New York with Gutzon Borglum and Hermon MacNeil, in Paris with Gauquié, Injalbert, and Rodin, and in Berlin with Von Euchtritz.

A Slavonic Dancer   23.106.3

Nude man, presumably the dancer Merio of the dance team Merio and Desha.

Bronze, height 12¾ in. Signed: Harriet W. Frishmuth. Dated 1921. Copyrighted; founder's mark: Roman Bronze Works N. Y.

REPLICAS: Wadsworth Atheneum, Hartford, Connecticut. According to the sculptor eight or ten replicas were cast in bronze.

EXHIBITED: Art Institute of Chicago, 1922; Pennsylvania Academy of the Fine Arts, Philadelphia, 1923; Texas Art Association, Dallas, 1923; Albright Art Gallery, Buffalo, 1923, 1924; Grand Central Art Galleries, New York, 1928.

PURCHASE, ROGERS FUND, 1923.

The Vine   27.66

The model for this figure of a nude bacchante was the dancer Desha, and the pose is reported to have been inspired by her dance "Modernistic Tango," which was last performed in New York at the Roxy Theater in 1931.

Bronze, height 83½ in. Signed: Harriet W. Frishmuth. Dated 1923. Copyrighted; founder's mark: Gorham Co. Founders.

REPLICAS: Los Angeles County Museum (bronze); private collection, Cincinnati (bronze); private collection, Riverside, Connecticut (bronze); private collection, Port Chester, New York (bronze); Brookgreen

Gardens, South Carolina (bronze reduction). According to the sculptor the original plaster model was destroyed after five large bronze replicas were made.

EXHIBITED: National Sculpture Society, New York, 1923; National Academy of Design, New York, 1923, Shaw Memorial Prize; Dallas Art Association, 1923; Pennsylvania Academy of the Fine Arts, Philadelphia, 1925; Brooklyn Museum, New York, 1926; Sesqui-Centennial Exposition, Philadelphia, 1926; Grand Central Art Galleries, New York, 1928.

PURCHASE, ROGERS FUND, 1927.

Chester Beach

1881-1956

BORN in San Francisco, California; died in New York. Beach studied architectural modeling at the Lick Polytechnic School and drawing at the Mark Hopkins Art Institute in San Francisco. In 1904 he went to Paris to study at the Académie Julian, returning to the United States in 1907. At this time he opened a studio in New York and worked mainly on statuettes of laboring men. In 1911 he returned to Europe and spent a year in Rome. He was awarded a medal of honor in 1924 by the Architectural League and the Potter Palmer Gold Medal by the Art Institute of Chicago in 1925. In 1938 he received the Lindsey Morris Memorial Prize of the National Sculpture Society for his work in medals. Beach was president of the National Sculpture Society and a member of the National Institute of Arts and Letters.

The Unveiling of Dawn   43.20

When this work, made in 1913, was first exhibited in New York a reviewer in the *New York American* commented that the idea was that of "the soul of man and woman struggling upward with the earth mists to the liberty and light of a fuller day. The method by which this conception is realized, so that much of the modeling is purposely undefined, while here and there a part is brought into significant clearness—the whole effect being one of suggestion demanding imagination on the spectator's part to evolve it—is, of course, derived from Rodin."

White marble, height 26½ in. Signed: C. Beach.

REPLICA: Detroit Institute of Arts (as Dawn; possibly this piece).

REFERENCE: *New York American* (May 26, 1913).

EXHIBITED: Armory Show, New York, 1913; Gorham Co., New York, c. 1913–1914; National Academy of Design, New York, *Winter Exhibition*, 1914; Pennsylvania Academy of the Fine Arts, Philadelphia, 1915; Art Institute of Chicago, 1915–1916; Cincinnati Art Museum, 1916.

GIFT OF MR. AND MRS. GEORGE W. DAVISON, 1943.

Other Works

10.34. Medal commemorating the Hudson-Fulton Celebration, with profiles of Henry Hudson and Robert Fulton. 1909. Bronze, diameter 1½ in. Gift of the Hudson-Fulton Celebration Commission, 1910.

37.167.1. Medal inscribed: In peace sons bury their fathers; (reverse) In war the fathers bury their sons. 1937. Bronze, diameter 2⅞ in. Gift of the Society of Medalists, 1937.

Alexander Finta

1881-1959

BORN in Turkeve, Hungary; died in California. Finta studied art in Budapest and later in Paris with Rodin and in Florence with Adolph Hildebrandt. On coming to the United

States he spent some time in New York and later moved to Los Angeles, where he was employed as a sculptor by one of the large motion picture companies.

Cardinal Hayes   27.153

Bust of Patrick Joseph, Cardinal Hayes (1867–1938), Archbishop of New York.

Marble, height 27 in. Signed: Finta. Dated 1927.

EXHIBITED: National Academy of Design, New York, *Annual Exhibition*, 1927.

GIFT OF VICTOR J. DOWLING AND ALEXANDER KONTA, 1927.

Arthur Lee

1881–1961

BORN in Trondjhem, Norway; died in Newtown, Connecticut. Lee was brought to the United States as a child of eight by his parents to live in St. Paul, Minnesota. He came to New York in 1901 to study at the Art Students League under Kenyon Cox and later studied in London and Paris at the École des Beaux Arts and traveled in Italy. On his return to New York he opened a studio in Greenwich Village and for many years was an instructor at the Art Students League.

Lee was awarded a number of medals for his work and won the Widener Gold Medal at the Pennsylvania Academy of the Fine Arts in 1924 and again in 1928. In his work he carried on the traditional sculptural interest in the human figure, idealized and sensitively modeled. He died after a long illness.

Volupté   24.293

A female torso.

Marble, height 38¾ in. Signed: Arthur Lee. Dated: Paris 1915. Inscribed: Volupte To R.L.C.

REPLICAS: Brooklyn Museum, New York (bronze?); private collection, New York (plaster reduction).

EXHIBITED: Wildenstein Galleries, New York, 1921 or 1922; National Sculpture Society,

New York, 1923; Pennsylvania Academy of the Fine Arts, Philadelphia, 1924, Widener Medal, and 1931; Art Institute of Chicago, 1926; Cincinnati Art Museum, 1926 (bronze); Brooklyn Museum, New York, 1930 (bronze).

ANONYMOUS GIFT, 1924.

Gaston Lachaise

1882–1935

BORN in Paris; died in New York. Lachaise was trained in the École Bernard Palissy and at the Académie Nationale des Beaux-Arts. He first exhibited at the Paris Salon of 1899. In 1906 he settled permanently in the United States. In this country he worked for a number of years as a studio assistant to the Boston sculptor Henry Hudson Kitson; later he worked for Paul Manship in the same capacity. Throughout this time, though he was working in the various academic traditions of his employers, he developed in his own studio a number of independent works, which remain a unique contribution to the development of modern sculpture. Especially notable among these works are his various studies of voluminous amplitude and matured forms embodied in his Standing Woman, La Montagne, Floating Woman, and their variations developed over a long period of years. In addition to these he executed a number of portrait heads, several garden sculptures, and reliefs for the R.C.A. Building in Rockefeller Center, New York City. He died just as he was beginning to design a monument for the Fairmount Park Art Association in Philadelphia.

La Montagne   49.70.224

A reclining nude woman.

Bronze, height 9 in., length 19⅝ in. Signed: G. Lachaise; dated 1924. Copyrighted; founder's mark: Roman Bronze Works N.Y.

THE ALFRED STIEGLITZ COLLECTION, 1949.

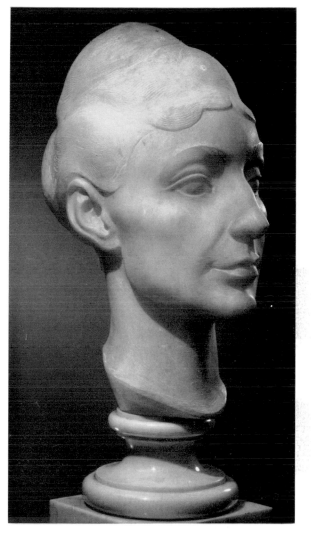

49.92.4

Georgia O'Keeffe   49.92.4

Head of Georgia O'Keeffe, the contemporary American artist.

Alabaster, height 23 in. Signed: G. Lachaise. Dated 1927. Copyrighted.

THE ALFRED STIEGLITZ COLLECTION, 1949.

Standing Woman   49.70.223

Bronze and chromium plate, height 13½ in. Signed: G. Lachaise. Copyrighted.

49.70.223

EXHIBITED: An American Place, New York.
THE ALFRED STEIGLITZ COLLECTION, 1949.

The Peacocks 50.173

A group of three peacocks, made about 1918.
Gilded bronze, height 23¼ in. Signed: G Lachaise. Dated 1922. Copyrighted; founder's mark: Roman Bronze Works N.Y.

REPLICA: Newark Museum, New Jersey.

REFERENCE: A. E. Gallatin, *Gaston Lachaise* (1924), pl. 14.

GIFT OF H. N. SLATER, 1950.

Elie Nadelman
1882–1946

BORN in Warsaw, Poland; died in Riverdale, New York. Nadelman studied art in Warsaw, Cracow, and Munich, and in Paris, where he became a friend of Leo and Gertrude Stein. Throughout his career he was more or less a solitary figure, and though some of his ideas and works anticipated and strongly influenced other better-known artists of the modern movement, Nadelman has seldom been given due credit for his originality and facility. He came to the United States in 1917 and became a citizen in 1927. In addition to his distinction as a sculptor he is to be remembered for his work in bringing together one of the first comprehensive collections of American folk art, which has since enriched a number of American museums and directed the attention of historians, designers, collectors, and museum officials to this important field.

Portrait of a Little Girl 46.51

Three-quarter standing figure, made about 1920.

Marble, height 30 in. Signed: Elie Nadelman.

GIFT OF MRS. STEVENSON SCOTT, 1946.

50.173

46.51

Mario Korbel

1882–1954

Born in Osik, Bohemia (Czechoslovakia); died in New York. Korbel studied sculpture in his native country. In 1900 he left for the United States, and returned to Europe in 1905 for study in Berlin, Munich, and Paris. He settled in New York in 1913 but spent some time in Cuba. While there, he made a statue of Alma Mater for Havana University, a medal of President Menocal, and a fountain for the president's garden.

Upon his return to the United States he was commissioned to make the sculpture for the George Booth estate at Birmingham, Michi-gan. He again left this country to work on this commission in Prague. Korbel was a member of the National Sculpture Society and the Architectural League of New York, an associate of the National Academy of Design, and was elected to the Legion of Honor.

Adolescence 33.102

Standing nude girl, a small version of a garden figure made for George Booth of Detroit.

Bronze, height 28½ in. Signed: Mario Korbel. Dated 1923. Founder's mark: Roman Bronze Works N.Y.

REPLICA: Detroit Institute of Arts (small size).

EXHIBITED: National Sculpture Society, New York, 1923.

GIFT OF ERNST ROSENFIELD, 1933.

Andante 28.119

Two nude girls dancing.

Bronze, height 43 in. Signed: Mario Korbel. Dated 1926. Copyrighted; founder's mark: Roman Bronze Works N.Y. No. 2.

REPLICAS: Detroit Institute of Arts (large size); Cleveland Museum of Art (small size); private collection, New York. According to the sculptor seven small-size replicas were cast in bronze in 1917. One was purchased by the Museum in 1918 but was exchanged in 1928 for the large size at the request of the sculptor, who considered it better.

REFERENCE: A. Patterson, *International Studio* 84 (1926):53.

EXHIBITED: Art Institute of Chicago; Detroit Institute of Arts; Cleveland Museum of Art; Pennsylvania Academy of the Fine Arts, Philadelphia; Fine Arts Building, New York, *Retrospective of American Art*, 1921.

PURCHASE, ROGERS FUND, 1918 AND BY EXCHANGE, 1928.

Fritz Kreisler 53.178

Bust of Kreisler (1875–1961), American violinist.

Marble, height 21¾ in. Signed: Mario Korbel. Dated 1942. Inscribed: [four bars of musical notation] Fritz Kreisler.

GIFT OF W. A. BAHR, 1952.

EXHIBITED: National Academy of Design, New York, *Winter Exhibition*, 1916.

PURCHASE, ROGERS FUND, 1918.

Clara Pfeifer Garrett

1882–

Mrs. Edmund A. Garrett. Born in Philadelphia. Clara Pfeifer Garrett studied sculpture at the St. Louis School of Fine Arts and at the École des Beaux-Arts in Paris with Mercié and Bourdelle.

Boy Teasing a Turtle   07.45

A fountain figure.

Bronze, height 15 in. Signed: C. Pfeifer. Dated: Paris 1903.

REFERENCE: *Catalogue of Sculpture* (Metropolitan Museum, 1908).

EXHIBITED: Paris, Salon of 1903; Louisiana Purchase Exposition, St. Louis, 1904.

PURCHASE, ROGERS FUND, 1907.

Harry Dickinson Thrasher

1883–1918

BORN in Cornish, New Hampshire; died in France. Thrasher studied sculpture with Augustus Saint-Gaudens. In 1911 he was awarded a scholarship at the American Academy in Rome. Later he worked with James Earle Fraser in New York. He was killed during the first World War.

Young Duck   18.120

Formerly called Figure of a Duck.

Bronze, height 11¼ in. Founder's mark: Roman Bronze Works.

REPLICA: Whitney Museum of American Art, New York (plaster).

Jo Davidson

1883–1952

BORN in New York; died in Tours, France. Davidson earned his own living at the age of fifteen and studied drawing at night. By means of scholarships, he was able to begin studying art. First he entered the Art Students League, where he studied under George de Forest Brush. As his parents thought that he should be in a profession, they sent him to study medicine at Yale, but he soon returned to New York to recommence his studies at the Art Students League. He worked on sculptures for the St. Louis Fair as an assistant to Hermon A. MacNeil.

Davidson received his first commission in 1905 and two years later went to Paris to study at the École des Beaux-Arts. He was then awarded a Hallgarten Scholarship, which enabled him to work independently. In the Salon of 1908 he exhibited The Violinist. In 1910 he returned to New York, where he had his first exhibition in America. He was awarded the Maynard Prize at the National Academy of Design Exhibition in 1934 and was made a Chevalier of the Legion of Honor.

Jules Semon Bache   49.7.120

Head of Jules S. Bache (1862–1944), American financier and art collector. The Bache collection of paintings and art objects was given to this Museum by the Bache Foundation in 1949.

Terra cotta, height 10 in. Signed: Jo Davidson. Dated 1936.

EXHIBITED: Metropolitan Museum, 1943; The American Academy of Arts and Letters, New York, 1948.

GIFT OF THE BACHE FOUNDATION, 1949.

Marshal Foch   50.145.41

This portrait of the French military commander Foch (1851–1929) was one of a pro-
jected series of portrait busts of the Allied
Chiefs of the first World War.

Bronze, height 9¾ in. Signed: Jo Davidson.
Inscribed: (on back) (11) Modélé au G.Q.G.
à Senlis Novembre 1918; (in front) Foch.
Copyrighted; founder's mark: C. Valsuani
Cire Perdue.

REPLICAS: Apparently several bronze replicas
were cast, but their location is not recorded.

REFERENCE: Jo Davidson, *Between Sittings*
(1951), pp. 132–141, ill. p. 86.

BEQUEST OF MARY STILLMAN HARKNESS,
1950.

Hunt Diederich

1884–1953

BORN in Hungary; died in New York. As a
child Diederich was educated in Switzerland
and at the age of sixteen was taken to Boston
to enter Milton Academy. He stayed there
only two years and then he went West and
lived as a cowboy in Wyoming, New Mexico,
and Arizona. Upon his return East, he went
to the Pennsylvania Academy of the Fine
Arts, where he studied with Paul Manship.
There he was awarded the Stewardson Prize
for sculpture.

   Diederich traveled widely in Africa and
Europe and finally settled in Paris for ten
years. In 1913 he exhibited his Greyhounds
at the Salon d'Automne. He was noted as a
designer and for his work in wrought iron
and his silhouettes.

Fighting Goats   55.103

Made in Paris in 1938.

Bronze, height 39 in. Signed: H Diederich.

REPLICA: Musée du Luxembourg, Paris.

55.103

EXHIBITED: Ferargil Galleries, New York.

PURCHASE, FLETCHER FUND, 1955.

Oscar Miestchaninoff

1884–1956

BORN in Vitebsk, Russia; died in New York.
Miestchaninoff developed an early interest in
sculpture, but this was discouraged by his
parents, until one day his father mistook one
of his portrait busts for a live person. Thereafter Miestchaninoff attended the Odessa

School of Fine Arts in Russia and later the École des Beaux-Arts in Paris. He was dissatisfied with both schools and remained for only short periods of time at each.

He exhibited regularly in Paris, where he made his home until 1944, when his first one-man show in New York was organized at the Wildenstein Galleries. Four years later Miestchaninoff became a naturalized citizen of the United States. In 1955 the Los Angeles County Museum held a large one-man exhibition of his work.

The Amazon   58.162.1

Executed in Paris in September 1928.

Granite, height 11¼ in.

EXHIBITED: Wildenstein Galleries, New York, 1944; Los Angeles County Museum, 1955, no. 15 in cat.

GIFT OF MRS. OSCAR MIESTCHANINOFF, 1958.

José de Creeft
1884–

BORN in Guadalajara, Spain. De Creeft studied in Madrid with the academic sculptor Don Augustin Querol and at the Académie Julian in Paris. He exhibited at the annual Paris Salons in 1907, 1909 to 1912, and 1914 and in later years at the Salon des Indépendants. He came to the United States in 1928, and teaches at the Art Students League. He is one of the leading exponents of the modern school of direct carving.

Maternity   42.171

Heads of a mother and child, carved direct in the stone in Paris in 1923.

Granite, height 28 in. Signed: J. de Creeft.

REFERENCES: *Artists for Victory* (a picture book of the prize winners, Metropolitan Museum, 1942); Jules Campos, *José de Creeft* (1945).

EXHIBITED: Paris, Salon d'Automne, 1923(?); Barcelona, 1923(?); Brooklyn Museum, New York, 1930; Passedoit Gallery, New York, 1935; Metropolitan Museum, *Artists for Victory*, 1942, First Prize.

PURCHASE, ROGERS FUND, 1942.

Émerveillement (Astonishment)
41.184

Kneeling figure of a nude woman, carved direct in the stone in 1941.

Green serpentine, height 18¾ in. Signed: José de Creeft.

REFERENCE: Jules Campos, *José de Creeft* 1945).

EXHIBITED: Passedoit Gallery, New York, 1941.

PURCHASE, MORRIS K. JESUP FUND, 1941.

42.171

Victor Salvatore

1884–1965

BORN in Italy. Salvatore studied sculpture with Charles Niehaus and A. Phimister Proctor in the United States. He is a member of the National Sculpture Society.

Bust of a Child: Top Knot   24.39

Made about 1912.

Marble, height 13½ in.

REPLICA: Private collection, New York (?) (bronze).

EXHIBITED: National Sculpture Society, New York, 1923; Art Institute of Chicago, 1923.

GIFT OF GEORGE DUPONT PRATT, 1924.

Meditation   28.45

Seated nude woman, made about 1912.

Marble, height 21½ in.

GIFT OF GEORGE DUPONT PRATT, 1928.

Paul Manship

1885–

BORN in St. Paul, Minnesota. Manship studied at the St. Paul School of Art and at the Pennsylvania Academy of the Fine Arts under Charles Grafly. He also worked as a studio assistant with Isadore Konti and Solon H. Borglum. In 1909 he was awarded a fellowship at the American Academy in Rome, where he worked for three years. He is a member of the American Academy of Arts and Letters, the National Academy of Design, and the National Sculpture Society, a fellow of the American Academy of Arts and Sciences, and a Chevalier of the Legion of Honor.

The tablet erected in 1920 in the Great Hall of the Museum by the Trustees to the memory of J. Pierpont Morgan was designed by Paul Manship in 1918 and cut in the stone by Manship's studio assistant Gaston Lachaise.

Centaur and Dryad   14.61

The pedestal of this statue is ornamented with scenes of nymphs and satyrs, animals, and griffins in low relief.

Bronze, height 28 in. Signed: Paul Manship. Dated 1913. Copyrighted.

REPLICAS: Fogg Museum of Art, Cambridge, Massachusetts; Detroit Institute of Arts; Smith College Museum of Art, Northampton, Massachusetts; City Art Museum, St. Louis.

REFERENCE: A. E. Gallatin, *Paul Manship* (1917).

EXHIBITED: National Academy of Design, New York, *Winter Exhibition*, 1913, Barnett Prize; Pennsylvania Academy of the Fine Arts, Philadelphia, 1914; Art Institute of Chicago, 1914; City Art Museum, St. Louis, 1915; Albright Art Gallery, Buffalo, 1915; Panama Pacific Exposition, San Francisco, 1915; Berlin Photographic Co., New York, 1916; Sesqui-Centennial Exposition, Philadelphia, 1926; Toronto Art Gallery, 1928;

14.61

48.149.28

48.149.27

Brookgreen Gardens, South Carolina, 1938.

PURCHASE, AMELIA B. LAZARUS FUND, 1913.

Dryad 52.126.5

A fragment of the Centaur and Dryad (preceding entry), made about 1913.

Bronze, height 12½ in. Founder's mark, R.B.W. [Roman Bronze Works].

GIFT OF THE ESTATE OF MRS. EDWARD ROBINSON, 1952.

Pauline Frances 16.42

A portrait relief, sometimes called The Artist's Daughter, Pauline Frances, Three Weeks Old, made in 1914.

Marble, height 13¾ in. (set in elaborate bronze frame designed by the sculptor).

REPLICA: Collection of the sculptor, New York (colored plaster).

REFERENCE: A. E. Gallatin, *Paul Manship* (1917).

EXHIBITED: Albright Art Gallery, Buffalo, 1915; City Art Museum, St. Louis, 1915; Berlin Photographic Co., New York, 1916; Brookgreen Gardens, South Carolina, 1938.

GIFT OF MRS. EDWARD F. DWIGHT, 1916.

Indian Hunter 48.149.28

A companion piece to the following entry, Pronghorn Antelope.

Bronze, height 13 in. Signed: Paul Manship. Dated 1914. Copyrighted; founder's mark: Roman Bronze Works N.Y.

REPLICAS: Private collection, Glen Cove, New York (heroic scale); Pratt Institute, Brooklyn, New York; City Art Museum, St. Louis; Art Institute of Chicago; Smith College Museum of Art, Northampton, Massachusetts.

REFERENCE: A. E. Gallatin, *Paul Manship* (1917).

EXHIBITED: Art Institute of Chicago, 1914; Albright Art Gallery, Buffalo, 1915.

BEQUEST OF GEORGE DUPONT PRATT, 1935.

Pronghorn Antelope 48.149.27

A companion piece to the preceding entry, Indian Hunter.

Bronze, height 12½ in. Signed: Paul Manship. Dated 1914. Copyrighted; founder's mark: Roman Bronze Works N.Y.

BEQUEST OF GEORGE DUPONT PRATT, 1935.

27.21.1

Wrestlers   27.21.1

Two nude men.

Bronze, height 11¼ in. Signed: Paul Manship. Dated 1915. Inscribed: To Edward D. Adams 6 20 1916. Copyrighted; founder's mark: Roman Bronze Works N.Y.

EXHIBITED: Albright Art Gallery, Buffalo, 1915; Berlin Photographic Co., New York, 1916; Pennsylvania Academy of the Fine Arts, Philadelphia, 1917.

GIFT OF EDWARD D. ADAMS, 1927.

59.54

Dancer and Gazelles 59.54

Bronze, height 32¼ in. Signed: Paul Manship. Dated 1916. Copyrighted.

REPLICAS: Of twelve replicas in this size, six are in the following museums: the Chicago Institute of Art, the Cleveland Museum of Art, the Detroit Institute of Arts, The Century Association, New York, the Musée du Luxembourg, Paris, and the Rhode Island School of Design, Providence; two replicas in life size are in the Toledo Museum of Art, Ohio, and the Corcoran Gallery of Art, Washington.

REFERENCE: E. Murtha, *Paul Manship* (1957), p. 158, pl. 17.

EXHIBITED: National Academy of Design, New York, 1917, Barnett Prize.

PURCHASE, FRANCIS LATHROP BEQUEST FUND, 1959.

29.162

Indian Hunter with Dog 29.162

This sculpture was originally designed for a large fountain in St. Paul, Minnesota.

Bronze, height 23¼ in. Signed: Paul Manship. Dated 1926. Copyrighted.

REPLICAS: According to the sculptor twelve bronze replicas were made.

REFERENCE: P. Vitry, *Paul Manship* (1927).

EXHIBITED: Toronto Art Gallery, 1928; Virginia Museum of Fine Arts, Richmond, 1936.

GIFT OF THOMAS COCHRAN, 1921.

James F. Ballard 27.147

This bust of James Franklin Ballard (1851–1931), American manufacturer of patent medicines, was made in 1927. In 1922 Ballard had presented his collection of rare Oriental rugs to this Museum.

Marble, height 21¼ in. Signed: Paul Manship. Inscribed: James F. Ballard.

REPLICA: Private collection, St. Louis (stone).

REFERENCE: J. Breck and F. Morris, *The James F. Ballard Collection of Rugs* (1923).

EXHIBITED: Toronto Art Gallery, 1928 (plaster); Virginia Museum of Fine Arts, Richmond, 1936 (plaster).

GIFT OF GUSTAVUS A. PFEIFFER, 1927.

Other Works

14.107. Medal inscribed: The Civic Forum; (reverse) George W. Goethals 1914 chief engineer Panama Canal for distinguished public service. 1914. Bronze, diameter 3⅛ in. Gift of the Civic Forum, 1914.

18.126. Plaquette inscribed: Art war relief. 1918. Bronze, 3 x 2½ in. Rogers Fund, 1918.

31.17. Medal commemorating the Southern Railway System centennial. 1930. Bronze, diameter 3½ in. Gift of Fairfax Harrison, 1931.

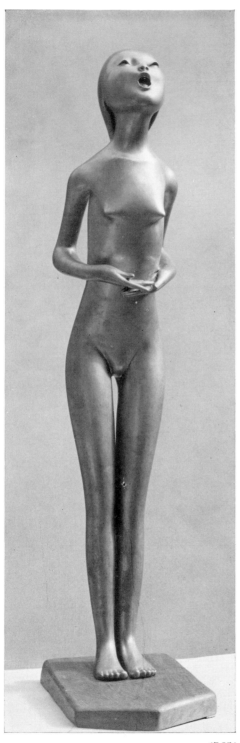

33.152.3. Medal inscribed: Hail to Dionysus who first discovered the magic of the grape. 1930. Bronze, diameter 2¹³⁄₁₆ in. Gift of the Society of Medalists, 1933.

29.38.1–9. Nine coins submitted in a competition for the coinage of the Irish Free State. 1927 (?). Bronze, diameter 4½ in. Gift of Paul Manship, 1929.

55.19.1, 2. Portrait medals of Edward Robinson and Elizabeth Robinson. Modeled 1923, cast 1954. Bronze, diameter 3¾ in. Gift of Paul Manship, 1955.

Tablet in Main Hall in memory of John Pierpont Morgan, with inscription and border of allegorical figures. Designed by Manship, executed by Gaston Lachaise. Limestone, 134 x 64 in. Erected by the Trustees of the Museum, 1920.

22.180.1, 2. Pair of candelabra, with figures of Adam and Eve and Vulcan and Venus.

Bronze, height 58½ in. E. C. Moore, Jr., Fund, 1922.

Hugo Robus

1885–1964

BORN in Cleveland, Ohio. Robus studied at the Cleveland School of Art, at the National Academy of Design in New York, and in Paris with Bourdelle.

Song   47.154

Figure of a standing nude girl, made in New York in 1934.

Brass, height 60 in. Signed (impressed under right heel): Hugo Robus.

EXHIBITED: Brooklyn Museum, New York, 1935 (plaster); Whitney Museum of American Art, New York, 1947.

PURCHASE, ROGERS FUND, 1947.

47.154

Edward Field Sanford, Jr.

1886–1951

BORN in New York; probably died in Williamsburg, Virginia. Beginning his education in sculpture at the age of twenty-one, Sanford studied at the Art Students League and the National Academy of Design for two years. Later he studied with Laurens at the Académie Julian in Paris and in Munich with Professor Bernhauer at the Royal Academy. He specialized in architectural sculpture and designed the sculptural decoration of the California State Capitol in Sacramento. When he was director of the Beaux-Arts Institute of Design in New York from 1923 to 1925, he was instrumental in reorganizing the Department of Sculpture. In 1933 ill health forced him to retire. He was a member of the National Sculpture Society and the Architectural League of New York.

Hercules   52.108

Bronze, height 24¼ in. Signed: Edward Field Sanford Jr. Dated 1916.

GIFT OF MRS. EDWARD F. SANFORD, JR., 1952.

Eugenie Frederika Shonnard

1886–

BORN in Yonkers, New York. Eugenie Shonnard studied at the New York School of Applied Design for Women and in Paris, where she received some criticism from Rodin and Bourdelle.

Head of a Breton Peasant   25.71

Also called Grandmother of Ploumanach, Old Lady of Ploumanach, and La Grand'mère.

25.71

Bronze, height 16 in. Signed: Eugenie F. Shonnard. Dated 1922. Founder's mark: [undecipherable name] Cire Perdue Paris.

REFERENCE: "Miss Shonnard Discovers Miss Shonnard," *Literary Digest* (June 7, 1924) (quoted from the Paris edition of the *New York Herald*).

EXHIBITED: Gorham Co., New York, 1925.

GIFT OF GEORGE DUPONT PRATT, 1925.

Emilio J. Sarniguet

1887–1943

BORN and died in Buenos Aires. Sarniguet began studying art in the Academia de la Sociedad Estimulo de Bellas Artes. In 1907 he was awarded a scholarship by the Jockey Club for his excellent studies of horses. This scholarship enabled him to study in Paris for several years, and a number of his works were shown at the annual Salon. Beginning in 1916, after his return to Argentina, he exhibited his

48.151

work at the official Salon in Buenos Aires. His work was awarded a Gold Medal at the Exposition Comunal de Artes Decorativas in Buenos Aires in 1926.

Martin Fierro   48.151

Martin Fierro is the title and the name of the hero of the famous Argentine poem of gaucho life written by José Hernandez and published in 1872. This equestrian statuette was probably the model for the Martin Fierro Monument in Argentina.

Bronze, height 16 in. Signed: E. J. Sarniguet. Founder's mark: Fund. Radelli y Gemelli Bs-Aires.

REFERENCE: J. Hernandez, *Martin Fierro, The Argentine Gaucho Epic*, translated by H. A. Holmes (1949).

GIFT OF THE FAMILY OF THE SCULPTOR PURSUANT TO A DIRECTION IN HIS WILL, 1948.

William Zorach

1887–

BORN in Eurburg, Lithuania. Zorach was brought to the United States at the age of four. He studied art at the Cleveland School of Art, at the National Academy of Design in New York, and in Paris. Zorach is known for his drawings and water colors as well as for his sculpture.

Seated Cat   37.121

Carved direct in the stone in 1937.

Swedish granite, height 17¾ in. Signed: Zorach.

REPLICAS: Two slightly varying versions, one cast in bronze, the other cut in marble, were made.

REFERENCES: P. Remington, *Met. Mus. Bull.*, old series 32 (1937):216; P. S. Wingert, *The Sculpture of William Zorach* (1938); William Zorach, *William Zorach, American Artists Group* (1945).

37.121

EXHIBITED: Art Institute of Chicago, 1928; National Exhibition of American Art, New York, 1937.

PURCHASE, EDWARD C. MOORE, JR., GIFT FUND, 1937.

Mother and Child   52.143

Made between 1927 and 1930; carved direct in the stone.

Spanish Florida Rosa marble, height 65 in.

REPLICA: Collection of the artist (plaster).

REFERENCES: "Continuity Between Tradition and Today," *Art Digest*, 5 (1931):12; W. Knowlton, *Creative Art* (Mar. 1931, supplement), p. 84; *American Magazine of Art*, 23 (1931):488; L. Cross, *London Studio*, 8 (1934):82; P. S. Wingert, *The Sculpture of William Zorach* (1938); W. Zorach, "The Background of an Artist," Part II, *Magazine of Art*, 34 (1941):234; W. Zorach, *Studio*, 127 (1944):185.

EXHIBITED: Downtown Gallery, New York, 1931; Art Institute of Chicago, 1931, 1934; Cleveland Museum of Art, 1937; Museum of Modern Art, New York, 1939.

PURCHASE, FLETCHER FUND, 1952.

Malvina Hoffman

1887–

BORN in New York. Malvina Hoffman studied in New York with Gutzon Borglum, Herbert Adams, and John W. Alexander, and in Paris with Rodin. She is a member of the National Academy of Design, the National Sculpture Society, the Three Arts Club, and the National Association of Women Painters and Sculptors.

A Modern Crusader   18.122

Head of a man (Colonel Milan Pribicevic of Yugoslavia) wearing a knitted helmet of the type used during the first World War. Made in 1918.

Bronze, height 19 in. Signed: Malvina Hoffman. Founder's mark: Roman Bronze Works Inc. N.Y.

REPLICA: Art Institute of Chicago.

REFERENCE: Malvina Hoffman, *Heads and Tales* (1937), pp. 127 f.

EXHIBITED: Pennsylvania Academy of the Fine Arts, Philadelphia, 1919 (as A Modern Crusader of Yugo-Slavia).

GIFT OF MRS. EDWARD H. HARRIMAN, 1918.

Pavlova Gavotte   26.105

Statuette of the Russian dancer Anna Pavlova (1885–1931), made in 1918 from an original modeled in 1915.

Wax, height 14 in. Signed: Malvina Hoffman.

REPLICAS: Art Museum, Stockholm, Sweden; private collection, London (formerly in collection of Lord Duveen); London Museum, Pavlova Memorial Collection (bronze); two in private collections, New York; Cleveland Museum of Art; Detroit Institute of Arts. According to the sculptor twelve replicas were made.

REFERENCES: *Catalogue of an Exhibition of American Sculpture* (Metropolitan Museum, 1918); Malvina Hoffman, *Heads and Tales* (1937), pp. 57–60.

EXHIBITED: Cincinnati Art Museum, 1915; National Sculpture Society, Buffalo (Albright Art Gallery), 1916; Pennsylvania Academy of the Fine Arts, Philadelphia, 1916; Metropolitan Museum, 1918.

PURCHASE, ROGERS FUND, 1926.

Paderewski the Artist   40.99

A portrait mask of the Polish pianist, composer, and statesman Jan Ignace Paderewski (1860–1951). Miss Hoffman has executed two other portraits of Paderewski, which are entirely different from each other and from this one—Paderewski the Friend and Paderewski the Statesman.

Bronze, height 16 in. Signed: Malvina Hoffman. Dated 1923. Copyrighted; founder's mark: Roman Bronze Works N.Y.

REPLICA: American Academy, Rome (bronze).

REFERENCES: Malvina Hoffman, *Heads and Tales* (1937); P. Remington, *Met. Mus. Bull.*, old series 35 (1940):206.

EXHIBITED: Pennsylvania Academy of the Fine Arts, Philadelphia, 1924; Albright Art Gallery, Buffalo, 1924.

PURCHASE, FRANCIS LATHROP BEQUEST FUND, 1940.

Mask of Anna Pavlova   35.107

Anna Pavlova (1885–1931), the Russian dancer.

Tinted wax, height 15½ in. Signed: M. Hoffman. Dated 1924. Copyrighted.

REPLICAS: Corcoran Gallery of Art, Washington (wax); Carnegie Institute, Pittsburgh (wax); Whitney Museum of American Art, New York (bronze); private collection, Chicago (wax). Several other examples were made.

REFERENCES: J. G. Phillips, *Met. Mus. Bull.*, old series 31 (1936):15; Malvina Hoffman, *Heads and Tales* (1937).

EXHIBITED: National Academy of Design, New York, 1924, Watrous Medal; Art Institute of Chicago, 1925; Pennsylvania Academy of the Fine Arts, Philadelphia, 1925; Brooklyn Museum, New York, 1929.

GIFT OF MRS. L. DEAN HOLDEN, 1935.

Ni-Polog   34.40.1

Portrait head of a Balinese dancer, made in 1931, a study for a life-size bronze statue in the series of ethnological types made for the Field Museum, Chicago.

Bronze, height 5½ in. Signed: M. Hoffman. Inscribed: Bali. Copyrighted; founder's mark: C.B.W. No 4.

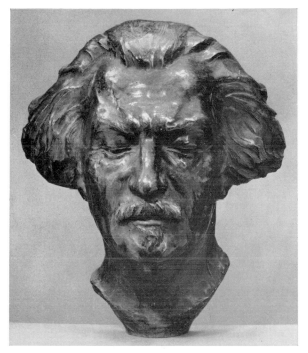

40.99

35.107

34.40.2

statue in the series of ethnological types made for the Field Museum, Chicago.

Bronze, height 23 in. Signed: Malvina Hoffman. Inscribed: Field Museum Chicago. Copyrighted; founder's mark: Alexis Rudier # III.

REPLICAS: Field Museum, Chicago (life-size bronze). Five replicas in the small size are in private collections.

REFERENCE: Malvina Hoffman, *Heads and Tales* (1937), p. 153.

PURCHASE, FRANCIS LATHROP BEQUEST FUND, 1934.

Bacchanale Russe   50.145.40

Pavlova and Mordkin posed for this sculpture, made in 1912, representing the moment of their entrance on stage in their famous Bacchanale, performed to the music of Glazunov.

REPLICAS: Three bronze replicas of the head in the small size are in private collections.

REFERENCES: *Met. Mus. Bull.*, old series 29 (1934):85; "Racial Types in Sculpture by Malvina Hoffman," *London Studio* (May 1934); Malvina Hoffman, *Heads and Tales* (1937), p. 258.

PURCHASE, FRANCIS LATHROP BEQUEST FUND, 1934.

Daboa   34.40.2

Statuette of a dancing girl of the Sara Tribe, Lake Chad District, Africa, made in Paris in 1931. This was a study for a life-size bronze

50. 145.40

Bronze, height 14⅛ in. Signed: Malvina Hoffman. Copyrighted; founder's mark: Roman Bronze Works N.Y.

REPLICAS: According to the sculptor three large versions and seven fourteen-inch casts were made of this work. A colossal version was purchased by the French government for the Luxembourg Gardens but was destroyed during the German occupation of Paris in 1941.

REFERENCE: Malvina Hoffman, *Heads and Tales* (1937), pp. 39, 56–59, 61.

EXHIBITED: Newark Museum, New Jersey, 1913; National Academy of Design, New York, 1917, Shaw Memorial Prize; Philadelphia Art Alliance, 1925; Currier Gallery of Art, Manchester, New Hampshire, 1937; Vose Gallery, Boston, 1937; Virginia Museum of Fine Arts, Richmond, 1937.

BEQUEST OF MARY STILLMAN HARKNESS, 1950.

Constance Whitney Warren

1888–1948

BORN in New York; died in Paris. Constance Warren's career began with sketching and designing posters. In 1911 she married Count Guy de Lasteyrie, and lived from then on in Paris. After the first World War she took up sculpture and exhibited regularly at the Salon, where she received several Honorable Mentions. In 1926 she executed a life-size equestrian statue of a cowboy for the State Capitol, Oklahoma City. Throughout her life horses and dogs remained her favorite subjects.

Hackney No. 1   54.53

Bronze, height 13½ in. Signed: C. W. Warren. Dated 1922. Copyrighted.

EXHIBITED: Ferargil Galleries, New York, 1953.

GIFT OF GEORGE HENRY WARREN, 1954.

Gleb Derujinsky

1888–

BORN in Smolensk, Russia. Derujinsky studied at the School for the Encouragement of Art and the Imperial Academy of Art in Petrograd and in Paris under Verlet and Injalbert. He came to the United States in 1919.

Sir John Lavery   34.136

Head of Sir John Lavery, R.A. (1856–1941), British portrait painter, cast in 1929.

Bronze, height 16 in. Signed: G. Derujinsky. Dated: London 1928. Founder's mark: Burton London.

REFERENCE: J. G. Phillips, *Met. Mus. Bull.*, old series 30 (1935):19.

EXHIBITED: Knoedler Galleries, London, 1928; Grand Central Art Galleries, New York, 1929; Wildenstein Galleries, New York, 1933.

PURCHASE, MORRIS K. JESUP FUND, 1934.

Frederick Warren Allen

1888–1961

BORN in North Attleboro, Massachusetts. Allen studied sculpture under Bela Lyon Pratt, and in Paris under Paul Landowski and Paul Bartlett. For many years he has been instructor in sculpture at the Museum of Fine Arts School in Boston. His work is represented in the Boston Museum of Fine Arts, and a number of his monuments have been erected in Boston and elsewhere in New England. He designed three colossal figures and a pediment for the New York County Court House.

Torso of a Woman   19.92

According to information in the *Boston Herald* at the time this bronze was acquired by the Museum, Allen held the opinion that "a portion of the human form can be so artistically unified as to render inclusion of head and limbs unnecessary," that "a structural fragment may . . . express the gesture of the whole." The original figure was shown at the Boston Art Club and was purchased by a group of members, who took up a subscription for it.

Bronze, height 10 in. Signed (on stump of right thigh): F. Allen. Dated 1914. Founder's mark illegible.

REPLICAS: Boston Museum of Fine Arts. Three replicas are said to be in private collections in Boston.

REFERENCE: *Boston Herald* (May 4, 1919).

EXHIBITED: Boston Art Club, 1914 (?); Albright Art Gallery, Buffalo, 1915; Detroit Museum of Art, 1916; Pennsylvania Academy of the Fine Arts, Philadelphia, 1919.

PURCHASE, ROGERS FUND, 1919.

George Winslow Blodgett

1888–1959?

Also known as George Winslow. Born in Faribault, Minnesota. Blodgett spent his early life in the lumber country of the Pacific Northwest. In 1926 he decided to become a sculptor, and, after a very brief period of instruction at the Beaux-Arts Academy in New York and at the Académie Julian in Paris, he began to work independently, recording various types of American Indians in the Southwest.

Head of a Tewa Indian   33.139

This head of Albert Lujan of the Taos Pueblo, modeled in 1930, is one of Blodgett's studies of Southwest Indians. The sculptor quoted Lujan as saying: "Since my father died I'm head of my family. My brothers and sisters and all their wives and mine, we are seven. We were all around when my father died. He said:

33·139

'Leave the door open—I'm going out that way. Albert, you are the oldest; you will look after your mother and sisters first, and your wife and yourself last.' "

Bronze (cast by Roman Bronze Works in 1931), height 10¼ in.

REPLICA: Brookgreen Gardens, South Carolina.

REFERENCES: D. Seabury, "George Winslow's Indian Sculpture," *Creative Art*, 12 (1933):366; P. Remington, *Met. Mus. Bull.*, old series 29 (1934):37; B. G. Proske, *Brookgreen Gardens, Sculpture* (1943).

EXHIBITED: Brooklyn Museum, New York, 1932; Arden Galleries, New York, 1933; Grand Central Art Galleries, New York, 1933.

PURCHASE, FRANCIS LATHROP BEQUEST FUND, 1933.

Bessie Stough Callender

1889–1951

BORN near Wichita, Kansas; died in New York. Bessie Callender studied in New York at the Art Students League and at the Cooper

Union. She went to Paris in 1926 and studied sculpture in the studio of Bourdelle and for three years with the animal sculptor Georges Hilbert. For a number of years she had a studio in London and exhibited her work at the Royal Academy. Examples of her animal sculpture are in the National Collection of Fine Arts in the Smithsonian Institution in Washington.

Eagle   54.75

Made about 1929.

Black Belgian marble, height 32½ in. Signed: Callender.

REFERENCE: H. Callender, *Fun Tomorrow, The Story of an Artist and a Way of Life* (1953), ill. at p. 54.

EXHIBITED: Royal Academy, London; Walker Art Gallery, Liverpool; Bradford Museum, Bradford, England; Paris, Salon des Indépendants.

GIFT OF HAROLD CALLENDER, 1954, IN MEMORY OF THE ARTIST.

Edgardo Simone

1890–1948

BORN in Brindisi, Italy; died in Los Angeles. Simone studied at the Institute of Fine Arts in Rome, the University of Rome, and the Art Institute in Naples. Before coming to the United States in 1924, he won many honors and prizes in Italy for his World War monuments there, in Brazil, and in Russia. In the United States he made many portrait busts of prominent men and worked on decorative sculpture for the Century of Progress Exposition in Chicago in 1933. The last years of his life were spent in California.

Theodore Dreiser   47.124

Portrait head of Theodore Dreiser (1871–1945), American novelist.

Bronze, height 16½ in. Inscribed: To T. Dreiser Edgardo Simone Dec 1944 original. Founder's mark: Roman Bronze Works Inc. N.Y.

REPLICA: According to the sculptor one replica in terra cotta was made.

EXHIBITED: Los Angeles County Museum; California Art Club, Los Angeles; Los Angeles Public Library, 1947.

GIFT OF MRS. THEODORE DREISER, 1947.

Bonnie McLeary

1890–

Mrs. Ernest W. Kramer. Born in San Antonio, Texas. Bonnie MacLeary studied in New York with Luis Mora and James Earle Fraser. Her father was James H. McLeary, an Associate Justice of the Supreme Court of Puerto Rico, where several of her monuments are located.

Aspiration   24.96

Standing figure of a nude woman, made in 1921.

Bronze, height 30¼ in. Signed: Bonnie McLeary. Copyrighted; founder's mark: American Art Foundry N.Y.

REPLICAS: According to the sculptor three bronze casts were made.

EXHIBITED: National Academy of Design, New York, 1921.

GIFT OF JAMIE NADAL, 1924.

Robert Laurent

1890–

BORN in Concarneau, France. Laurent studied with Hamilton Easter Field and Maurice Sterne and at the British Academy in Rome.

A Singer   41.178.7

Statuette of a woman.

Bronze, height 13¾ in. Signed: Laurent. Dated: Brooklyn N.Y. 1939. Founder's mark: Br Foundry N.Y.

PURCHASE, MORRIS K. JESUP FUND, 1941.

Leo Friedlander

1890–

BORN in New York. Friedlander studied at the Art Students League in New York, at the École des Beaux-Arts in Paris, in Brussels, and at the American Academy in Rome.

24 50

A Bacchante   24.50

Figure of a standing nude woman.

Bronze, height 20¾ in. Signed: Leo Friedlander, Sc. Dated 1916. Copyrighted; founder's mark: Roman Bronze Works N.Y.

EXHIBITED: Metropolitan Museum, 1918; Pennsylvania Academy of the Fine Arts, Philadelphia, 1919; Art Institute of Chicago, 1920; Brooklyn Museum, New York, 1930.

PURCHASE, ROGERS FUND, 1924.

Other Works

50.1.1. Medal inscribed: Harmony; (reverse) Creates tranquility. 1949. Bronze, diameter 2⅞ in. Gift of the Society of Medalists, 1950.

Paul Jennewein

1890–

Carl Paul Jennewein. Born in Stuttgart, Germany. Jennewein came to the United States at the age of seventeen and studied sculpture at the Art Students League in New York and at the American Academy in Rome.

Cupid and Gazelle   33.162

Bronze, height 28 in. Signed: C. P. Jennewein. Dated: Roma 1919. Copyrighted; founder's mark: P. B. Co. Munchen Made In Germany.

REPLICAS: Houston Art Museum, Texas; Brookgreen Gardens, South Carolina; Baltimore Museum of Art; Cranbrook Academy of Art, Bloomfield Hills, Michigan; Montclair Art Museum, New Jersey. According to the sculptor sixteen replicas were cast in bronze.

REFERENCE: B. G. Proske, *Brookgreen Gardens, Sculpture* (1943).

EXHIBITED: American Academy, Rome, 1920, Art Institute of Chicago, 1921; Architectura; League, New York, 1921; Scott and Fowlesl New York, 1921; Baltimore Museum of Art,

1923; National Sculpture Society, New York, 1923, Dallas Art Association, Texas, 1925.

PURCHASE, ROGERS FUND, 1933.

Other Works

33.152.13. Medal inscribed: Gloria; (reverse) Fama. 1933. Bronze, diameter 2¾ in. Gift of the Society of Medalists, 1933.

Georg John Lober

1892–1961

BORN in Chicago; died in New York. Lober's early art training began in New York at the National Academy of Design and the Beaux-Arts Institute of Design. His teachers were A. Stirling Calder, Hermon MacNeil, Gutzon Borglum, and Evelyn Longman. He won several prizes, among them the sculpture prize of the Allied Artists of America in 1931, the Jenkins Prize for sculpture at the Grand Central Art Galleries in 1931, and the National Arts Club Medal in 1935. He was head of the sculpture department of the Grand Central School of Art and a member of the National Academy of Design, the National Sculpture Society, the Architectural League of New York, and the American Numismatic Society and served for many years on the New York City Art Commission.

Eve   26.55

Standing figure of a nude woman.

Bronze, height 17¼ in. Signed: Lober. Dated 1918. Copyrighted; founder's mark: American Art Foundry N.Y.

REPLICA: Private collection, New York (marble).

EXHIBITED: National Academy of Design, New York, 1918; Pennsylvania Academy of the Fine Arts, Philadelphia, 1919, 1920, 1929 (marble); National Sculpture Society, New York, 1923; Baltimore Museum of Art, 1923; Brooklyn Museum, New York, 1930.

33.162

GIFT OF EDWARD BRUCE DOUGLAS IN MEMORY OF HIS FATHER WALTER DONALD DOUGLAS, 1926.

Antonio Salemme

1892–

BORN in Gaeta, Italy. Salemme studied sculpture in Boston from 1908 to 1912, in Rome with Angelo Zarelli from 1912 to 1919, and in Paris from 1932 to 1934.

Head of a Woman   46.62

Portrait of a woman, made in 1945.

Terra cotta; height 11 in. Signed: Antonio Salemme.

GIFT OF CHAUNCEY STILLMAN, 1946.

Enea Biafora

1892–1953?

BORN in San Giovanni in Fiore, Italy. Biafora first studied with his father, a sculptor, and in 1907 at the Institute of Fine Arts in Naples. Later he taught drawing. He came to the United States in 1914 and worked in the studios of George Grey Barnard, Malvina Hoffman, and Paul Manship.

The Little Centauress   25.88

This statuette of a young centauress with a baby satyr on her back and a set of Panpipes in her hand was made about 1917.

Bronze, height 13½ in.

EXHIBITED: National Academy of Design, New York, *Winter Exhibition*, 1922; Pennsyl-

vania Academy of the Fine Arts, Philadelphia, 1923; Art Institute of Chicago, 1923; Albright Art Gallery, Buffalo, 1923.

GIFT OF MRS. HARRY PAYNE BINGHAM, 1925.

Oronzio Maldarelli

1892–1963

BORN in Naples; died in New York. Maldarelli was brought to the United States at the age of nine. He studied art at the National Academy of Design, Cooper Union, and at the Beaux-Arts Institute of Design in New York. From 1931 to 1933 he studied in Paris on a Guggenheim Scholarship.

Reclining Figure   41.178.6

Figure of a nude woman, made in Paris in 1931.

Marble, height 11¾ in., length 17¾ in. Signed: O. Maldarelli.

PURCHASE, MORRIS K. JESUP FUND, 1941.

Bianca No. II   53.126

Figure of a nude woman, made about 1950.

Bronze, height 27¾ in. Signed: O. Maldarelli sc.

REPLICAS: Several bronze casts were made from a small-scale model similar to but not identical with this figure.

REFERENCE: A. C. Ritchie, *Sculpture of the Twentieth Century* (1952), ill. p. 190.

EXHIBITED: Pennsylvania Academy of the Fine Arts, Philadelphia, *Annual Exhibition*, 1951; Whitney Museum of American Art, New York, *Annual Exhibition*, 1951; Museum of Modern Art, São Paulo, Brazil, 1951; Midtown Gallery, New York, 1952; Philadelphia Museum of Art, 1952; Art Institute of Chi-

53.126

cago, 1953; Museum of Modern Art, New York, 1953.

Purchase, Fletcher Fund, 1953.

Boris Lovet-Lorski
1894–

Born in Lithuania. Lovet-Lorski studied art in St. Petersburg from 1913 to 1917, in the United States from 1920 to 1925, and in Paris from 1925 to 1934. He now lives in New York.

Feodor Chaliapin 38.151

Portrait head of the Russian singer Chaliapin (1873–1938), modeled in 1938 from sketches made at Salzburg in 1937.

Bronze, height 23¼ in. Signed: Lovet-Lorski. Founder's mark: coat of arms—crowned shield with bear passant and anchor above; Cast by René Carvillani, Paris.

Replica: Collection of the sculptor, New York.

Exhibited: Wildenstein Galleries, New York, 1938.

Purchase, Francis Lathrop Bequest Fund, 1938.

Ariadne 52.151

Ariadne, in Greek mythology, was the daughter of Minos, king of Crete.

Marble, height 34½ in. Signed: Lovet-Lorski.

Replica: A black marble replica was exhibited in New York in 1945.

Reference: Paul S. Wingert, "Sculpture Festival in New York," *Magazine of Art*, 33 (1940):297, ill.

Exhibited: Whitney Museum of American Art, New York, 1940; Art Institute of Chicago, 1941; Metropolitan Museum, 1942; Wildenstein Galleries, New York, 1945.

Anonymous Gift, 1952.

52.151

John Bernard Flannagan
1895–1942

Born in Fargo, North Dakota; died in New York. Most of Flannagan's life was spent in extreme poverty. In his youth he studied painting at the Minneapolis Institute of Fine Arts with Robert Koehler. After five years with the Merchant Marine (1917–1922) he received some instruction from the painter Arthur B. Davies, who encouraged him to attempt wood-carving. About 1928 he began to carve in stone. His career came abruptly to an end when he committed suicide after undergoing four serious brain operations.

In one of his letters Flannagan stated his credo, which may well stand as representing the modern point of view as opposed to that of the modelers in clay of a previous generation: "My aim is to produce sculpture as direct and swift in feeling as drawing—sculpture with such ease, freedom, and simplicity that it hardly seems carved but rather to have endured so always. This accounts for my preference for field stone; its very rudeness seems to me more in harmony with simple direct statement. There are often necessary compromises, but the shape of the stone does not determine the design; more often the design dictates the choice of the stone. I would like my sculpture to appear as rocks, left quite untouched and natural. . . . Such qualities of humor or the grotesque or whatever may be found therein are for the most part accidental and subordinate to a conception purely sculptural." Flannagan's aims and beliefs as an artist are also admirably summed up in a brief statement, "The Image in the Rock," written shortly before his death.

Figure of Dignity—Irish Mountain Goat   41.47

In his "The Image in the Rock" the sculptor wrote: "As design, the eventual carving involuntarily evolves from the eternal nature of the stone itself, an abstract linear and cubical fantasy out of the fluctuating sequence of consciousness, expressing a vague general memory of many creatures, of human and animal life in its various forms. It partakes of the deep pantheistic urge of kinship with all living things and fundamental unity of life, a unity so complete it can see a figure of dignity even in the form of a goat." This statue was carved direct by the sculptor about 1932.

Granite, with horns of cast aluminum, height 53¾ in.

REFERENCES: P. Remington, *Met. Mus. Bull.*, old series 36 (1941):101; "Shilling Fund Award," *Art Digest* (May 1, 1941); "Shilling Fund Purchases a Flannagan Statue," *Art*

41.47

News (May 1, 1941); "Figure of Dignity to Metropolitan," *Magazine of Art* (May 1941); J. B. Flannagan, "The Image in the Rock," *The Sculpture of John B. Flannagan* (exhibition cat., Museum of Modern Art, 1942).

EXHIBITED: Chicago Arts Club, 1934; Sculptors Guild, New York, 1938; Philadelphia Museum of Art, 1940; Carnegie Institute, Pittsburgh, 1941; Museum of Modern Art, New York, 1942.

GIFT OF THE ALEXANDER SHILLING FUND, 1941.

Allan Clark

1896–1950

BORN in Missoula, Montana. Clark studied sculpture at the Chicago Art Institute under Albin Polasek and in the Orient.

Mei Kwei   27.197

Portrait head of a Chinese girl.

Mahogany, height 11½ in. Signed: Allan Clark. Dated 1927.

REFERENCE: John Steele, *International Studio*, 89 (1928):61.

EXHIBITED: Fogg Art Museum, Cambridge, Massachusetts, 1927; Wildenstein Galleries, New York, 1927.

PURCHASE, ROGERS FUND, 1927.

Kongo Voodoo   33.30

Statuette of an African dancer.

Bronze, height 22 in. Signed: Allan Clark. Dated 1927. Founder's mark: Roman Bronze Works N.Y.

REPLICAS: According to the sculptor twelve bronze casts were made.

GIFT OF CHARLES BAIN HOYT, 1933.

33.30

Gladys Edgerly Bates

1896–

BORN in Hopewell, New Jersey. Gladys Edgerly Bates studied at the Pennsylvania Academy of the Fine Arts under Charles Grafly and Albert Laessle and at the Corcoran Gallery of Art in Washington.

Morning   42.174

Reclining figure of a woman, made in 1935.

Tinted plaster, height 28 in., length 49 in.

REFERENCE: *Artists for Victory* (a picture book of the prize winners, Metropolitan Museum, 1942).

EXHIBITED: Art Institute of Chicago, 1935, Honorable Mention, and *Half a Century of American Art*, 1939; Dallas Museum of Fine Arts, *Texas Centennial Exhibition*, 1936; National Academy of Design, New York, 1942; Metropolitan Museum, *Artists for Victory*, 1942, purchase prize.

PURCHASE, ROGERS FUND, 1942.

Suzanne Silvercruys

1898–

BORN in Maeswyck, Belgium. Suzanne Silvercruys came to this country as a young girl and became a naturalized citizen in 1922. She studied at the Yale School of Fine Arts and at the American Academy in Rome.

John Buchan, Lord Tweedsmuir

39.139

Bust of John Buchan (1875–1940), British author and diplomat.

Bronze, height 16¼ in. Signed: Suzanne Silvercruys. Dated: Ottawa, 1938.

REFERENCE: P. Remington, *Met. Mus. Bull.*, old series 34 (1939):289.

GIFT OF MRS. LAURENT OPPENHEIM, 1939.

Alexander Calder

1898–

BORN in Philadelphia. Alexander Calder is the son of the sculptor A. Stirling Calder. He studied mechanical engineering at the Stevens Institute of Technology and later studied painting at the Art Students League in New York.

Mobile

42.176

The mobile is perhaps best described in Jean Paul Sartre's words: "Une petite fête locale,

un objet défini par son mouvement et qui n'existe pas en dehors de lui, une fleur qui se fane dès qu'elle s'arrête, un jeu pur de mouvement comme il y a de purs jeux de lumière." (A little private celebration, an object defined by its movement and having no other existence, a flower that fades when it ceases to move, a pure play of movement in the sense that we speak of a pure play of light.) This mobile was made in 1942.

Steel and aluminum, occupies and moves in cylindrical volume of space 62 in. high and 70 in. in diameter.

REFERENCES: *Artists for Victory* (a picture book of the prize winners, Metropolitan Museum, 1942); Jean Paul Sartre, *Style en France*, no. 5 (1947).

EXHIBITED: Metropolitan Museum, *Artists for Victory*, 1942, purchase prize.

PURCHASE, ROGERS FUND, 1942.

Red Gongs—a Mobile   55.181 a–f

Sheet aluminum, sheet brass, steel rod and wire, red paint, length c. 144 in.

PURCHASE, FLETCHER FUND, 1955.

Beniamino Bufano

1898–

BORN in San Fele, Italy. Bufano was brought to the United States in 1901 and at an early age went to work in a wood-carving shop in New York. He studied at the Art Students League and was later studio assistant to Herbert Adams, James Earle Fraser, and Paul Manship. Bufano is credited with being the first sculptor to use stainless steel. He lived in the Orient for a number of years, where he studied Chinese glazes and pottery processes. His best-known work is the statue of Sun Yat Sen in San Francisco, where much of his work has been done and where he now lives.

24.42

42.177

Honeymoon Couple   24.42

This work, formerly called by the Museum Chinese Man and Woman and also known as The Chinese Couple and Chinese Friends, was made in 1921 from a design made in 1919 or 1920.

Glazed stoneware, height 31½ in.

REPLICAS: San Francisco Museum of Art (stoneware). According to the sculptor there is also a painted plaster replica.

REFERENCES: P. Ackerman, *International Studio*, 80 (1925):375; *Met. Mus. Bull.*, old series 20 (1925):58; *Beniamino Bufano ... Biography and Works* (California Art Research, series 1, part 14, 1937).

EXHIBITED: Arden Galleries, New York, 1925; Art Institute of Chicago, c. 1926–1927; City Art Museum, St. Louis, 1926–1927(?); Paris, Salon d'Automne, 1927(?); Brooklyn Museum, New York, 1930–1932(?).

GIFT OF GEORGE BLUMENTHAL, 1924.

Frances Kent Lamont

1899–

BORN in Bronxville, New York. Frances Lamont studied with Solon Borglum and Mahonri Young.

Gallic Cock   42.177

Statue of a fighting cock, a national symbol of France, made in 1939 and 1940.

Polished brass (cast by Bedford Bronze Foundry), height 15 in.

REPLICA: Cranbrook Museum, Bloomfield Hills, Michigan.

REFERENCE: *Artists for Victory* (a picture book of the prize winners, Metropolitan Museum, 1942).

EXHIBITED: Philadelphia Museum of Art, 1940; Metropolitan Museum, *Artists for Victory*, 1942, purchase prize.

PURCHASE, ROGERS FUND, 1942.

Helene Sardeau

1899–

BORN in Antwerp, Belgium. Helene Sardeau studied at the Art Students League and the School of American Sculptors. She is a member of the Sculptors Guild.

Kneeling Woman   56.192

Bronze, height 28¼ in. Signed: Sardeau. Dated 1955.

GIFT OF MADAME HELENA RUBINSTEIN, 1956.

Henry Kreis

1899–1963

BORN in Essen, Germany; died in Essex, Connecticut. Kreis studied under Paul Wackerle in Munich at the State School of Applied Art. He came to the United States in 1923 and studied with Paul Manship at the Beaux-Arts Institute of Design in New York.

Indian Summer   42.175

Figure of a seated woman, carved direct in the stone in 1937.

Brownstone, height 21½ in. Signed: Henry Kreis.

REFERENCE: *Artists for Victory* (a picture book of the prize winners, Metropolitan Museum, 1942).

EXHIBITED: Philadelphia Museum of Art, 1940; Whitney Museum of American Art, New York, 1940; Metropolitan Museum, *Artists for Victory*, 1942, purchase prize.

PURCHASE, ROGERS FUND, 1942.

Other Works

48.4.1. Medal of the Wise and Foolish Virgins. 1947. Bronze, diameter 2⅞ in. Gift of the Society of Medalists, 1948.

56.192

Maria Martins

1900–

Senhora Carlos Martins Pereira e Souza. Born in Minas Geraes, Brazil. Maria Martins studied sculpture in Belgium.

Saint Francis   42.75

This statue of Saint Francis of Assisi was made in Washington in 1940. The inscription is part of a verse from Saint Francis's Canticle of the Sun: Laudato si mi signore per sora nostra morte corporale, de la quale nullu homo viventi po skappare; guai a quilli ke morrano ne le peccata mortali; beati quilli ke se trovara

ne le tue sanctissime voluntati, ke la morte secunda nol farra male. (Praised be my Lord for our sister, the death of the body, from whom no man escapeth. Woe to him who dieth in mortal sin. Blessed are they who are found walking by thy most holy will, for the second death will have no power to do them harm.)

Brazilian rosewood (jacaranda), height 73½ in. Inscribed: Laudato si mi signore per sora nostra morte.

EXHIBITED: Riverside Museum, New York, 1940; Corcoran Gallery of Art, Washington, 1941; Valentine Gallery, New York, 1942.

ANONYMOUS GIFT, 1942.

Albert T. Stewart

1900–

BORN in Kensington, England. Stewart came to the United States at the close of the first World War and studied sculpture at the Beaux-Arts Institute of Design in New York. Later he worked with MacMonnies, and he was for several years a studio assistant for Paul Manship.

38.18

42.180

Hawk 26.184

Bronze, height 7½ in. Signed: Stewart. Founder's mark: Kunst Foundry N Y.

GIFT OF EDWIN DE T. BECHTEL, 1926.

Silver King 38.18

A portrait of a polar bear.

Silvered bronze, height 13½ in. Signed: Albert Stewart. Dated 1927. Founder's mark: Kunst F'dry N Y.

REPLICA: Private collection, New York (marble).

EXHIBITED: National Academy of Design, New York, 1927, Speyer Prize; Pennsylvania Academy of the Fine Arts, Philadelphia, 1928, Widener Medal; Art Institute of Chicago, 1928; Lamar Gallery, New York, 1930; Ferargil Gallery, New York, 1934.

GIFT OF EDWIN DE T. BECHTEL, 1938.

Other Works

36.132.1. Medal inscribed: Peace; (reverse) Man seeks to turn from the savagery of war. 1936. Bronze, diameter 2⅞ in. Gift of the Society of Medalists, 1936.

Richmond Barthe

1901–

BORN in Bay St. Louis, Mississippi. Barthe studied at the Art Institute of Chicago, at the Art Students League in New York, at Xavier University, and with Charles Schroeder.

Boxer   42.180

A statuette.

Bronze (cast in 1942), height 16 in. Signed: Barthe. Founder's mark: Cellini Bronze Works, Brooklyn, N.Y.

REFERENCE: *Artists for Victory* (a picture book of the prize winners, Metropolitan Museum, 1942).

EXHIBITED: De Porres Inter-racial Center, New York, 1941 (plaster); Metropolitan Museum, *Artists for Victory*, 1942 (bronze), purchase prize.

PURCHASE, ROGERS FUND, 1942.

Seymour Lipton

1903–

BORN in New York. Lipton has had no formal training as a sculptor and is entirely self-taught. He is Instructor in Sculpture at the New School for Social Research in New York.

Pioneer   58.61

An abstract sculpture, made in 1957.

Nickel-silver on Monel metal, height 94 in.

58.61

EXHIBITED: International Exposition of Art, Venice, 1958; Betty Parsons Gallery, New York, 1958.

GIFT OF MRS. ALBERT A. LIST, 1958.

Eugenie Gershoy

1903–

BORN in Krivoi Rog, Russia. Eugenie Gershoy studied art at Columbia University and at the Art Students League in New York.

An Equestrienne   42.181

Statuette of an acrobatic bareback rider, made in 1938.

Synthetic papier-mâché, polychromed, height 20 in. Signed: Eugenie Gershoy.

REFERENCE: *Artists for Victory* (a picture book of the prize winners, Metropolitan Museum, 1942).

EXHIBITED: Robinson Galleries, New York, 1938; Whitney Museum of American Art, New York, 1938; Metropolitan Museum, *Artists for Victory*, 1942, purchase prize.

PURCHASE, ROGERS FUND, 1942.

Isamu Noguchi

1904–

BORN in Los Angeles, California. Noguchi was taken to Japan as a child but returned to the United States at the age of thirteen. For a time he worked with Gutzon Borglum (see p. 100), who told him he could never become a sculptor. He then turned his attention to studying medicine but with the encouragement of the sculptor Onorio Ruotolo again tried his hand at sculpture. He later won a Guggenheim Scholarship and went to Paris to study with Brancusi.

34.97

Angna Enters   34.97

This head of the contemporary American dancer, poet, and artist was cast by Anton Kunst in 1932.

Bronze, height 11¼ in. Signed: Isamu. Dated 1931.

REFERENCE: J. G. Phillips, *Met. Mus. Bull.*, old series 29 (1934):197.

EXHIBITED: New York, 1931 (?).

PURCHASE, MORRIS K. JESUP FUND, 1934.

Kouros   53.87

An abstraction, made in 1944 and 1945.

Marble, height 117 in.

REFERENCE: R. B. Hale, *Met. Mus. Bull.*, new series 16 (1957):18.

EXHIBITED: Museum of Modern Art, New York, 1946.

PURCHASE, FLETCHER FUND, 1953.

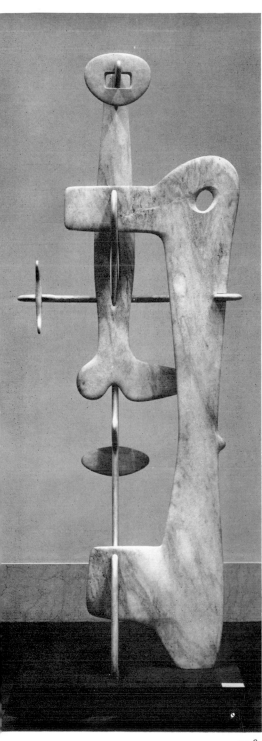

Chaim Gross

1904–

BORN in Wolowa, Austria. Gross studied sculpture at the Art Students League, at the Beaux-Arts Institute of Design, and at the Educational Alliance Art School, all in New York.

Lillian Leitzel   42.172

This figure of Lillian Leitzel (1894–1931), a famous circus acrobat, was made in 1938.

Macassar ebony, height 52 in. Signed: Ch. Gross.

53.87   42.172

REFERENCES: *Artists for Victory* (a picture book of the prize winners, Metropolitan Museum, 1942); J. V. Lombardo, *Chaim Gross, Sculptor* (1949).

EXHIBITED: Whitney Museum of American Art, New York, 1939; Museum of Modern Art, New York, 1939; Metropolitan Museum, *Artists for Victory*, 1942, purchase prize.

PURCHASE, ROGERS FUND, 1942.

Girl on Wheel   42.14

An acrobat riding on a single wheel, made in 1940.

Wood (lignum vitae?), height 29 in. Signed: Chaim Gross.

REPLICAS: Ten small reproductions in wood were made.

REFERENCE: J. V. Lombardo, *Chaim Gross, Sculptor* (1949).

PURCHASE, MORRIS K. JESUP FUND, 1942.

Joy Buba

1904–

Margaret Flinsch Buba. Born in Huntington, Long Island, New York. As a child Mrs. Buba studied sculpture with Abastenia St. Leger Eberle in New York and later went to the Frankfort Art Academy, where she worked under Louise Schmidt and Angelo Jank.

David Mannes   47.53

This portrait of the American musician (1866–1959) was made in 1943. It was purchased by the Trustees of the Museum on the occasion of Mannes's retirement after thirty years as conductor of the annual series of free public concerts at the Museum.

Tinted cast stone with onyx base, height 12 in.

PURCHASE, MORRIS K. JESUP FUND, 1947.

55.204

José de Rivera

1904–

BORN near Baton Rouge, Louisiana. De Rivera studied drawing and painting in Chicago under John Norton and painted in Europe and North Africa. He is a member of the Sculptors Guild.

Homage to the World of Minkowski
55.204

The sculptor explains that the Russian mathematician and physicist Herman Minkowski was the first to state that time and space could not be understood separately, since they are one. This unity is known in science as "the world of Minkowski." This sculpture was made about 1955.

Chrome, nickel, and stainless steel, height 14⅞ in.

REFERENCE: *Art Digest*, 29 (1955):22.

EXHIBITED: Grace Borgenicht Gallery, New York, 1955; Museum of Modern Art, New York, 1956.

PURCHASE, FLETCHER FUND, 1955.

42.178

REFERENCE: *Artists for Victory* (a picture book of the prize winners, Metropolitan Museum, 1942).

EXHIBITED: Metropolitan Museum, *Artists for Victory*, 1942, purchase prize.

PURCHASE, ROGERS FUND, 1942.

Herbert Ferber

1906–

BORN in New York City. Ferber studied art at the Beaux-Arts Institute of Design in New York.

To Fight Again   42.178

Group of three figures, carved direct in the stone.

Granite, height 22 in. Signed: Ferber. Dated 1940.

David Smith

1906–1965

BORN in Decatur, Illinois. Smith studied at Ohio University, George Washington University, and the Art Students League under J. Matulke. He also studied and worked in Greece.

Tanktotem II (Sounding)   53.93

The sculptor describes this work as "a totem of a tank part related to sounds. . . . It is one

53·93

of a series of two Tanktotems related only in the sense that their points of reality and conceptual origin started with dish-shaped steel of a convex nature related to the concave ends of a tank."

Steel and bronze, height 80½ in. Signed: David Smith. Dated 1952–53. Inscribed: Tanktotem II.

REFERENCE: S. Geist, "Man of Iron," *Art Digest*, 27 (Feb. 1953):16.

EXHIBITED: Kootz Gallery, New York, 1953.

PURCHASE, FLETCHER FUND, 1953.

Frederick Charles Shrady

1907–

BORN in New York. Shrady, the son of Henry Merwin Shrady (see p. 109) began studying art in 1928 at the Art Students League. In 1931 he studied under Yasushi Tanaka in Paris, and in 1934 he went to Florence.

The Very Reverend Martin C. D'Arcy, S.J.   54·73

The Very Reverend Martin D'Arcy was formerly the Master of Campion Hall, the private hall for Jesuits in Oxford, and is now Provincial of the Society of Jesus in England. He is the prime authority on the works of Gerard Manley Hopkins. This head was made in 1953.

Bronze with marble base, height 12⅜ in. Signed (back of collar): F. C. Shrady.

GIFT OF MATTHEW J. MURRAY, 1954.

Koren der Harootian

1909–

BORN in Ashodavan, Armenia. Harootian was brought to the United States as a child. He studied painting and sculpture at the School of the Worcester Art Museum, Massachusetts, and now works in New York.

Prometheus and the Vulture   48.142

Prometheus was punished by Zeus for stealing fire from the gods by being bound to Mount Caucasus, where a vulture plucked at his liver.

Westfield green marble, height 63 in. Signed (on plinth): Koren der Harootian.

REFERENCE: *Met. Mus. Bull.*, new series 7 (1949):150, ill.

48.142

EXHIBITED: New York, *Harootian*, one-man outdoor show, 1948; Sculptors Guild, New York, 1948.

GIFT OF HAIK KAVOOKJIAN, 1948.

Eleanor Platt

1910–

BORN in Woodbridge, New Jersey. Eleanor Platt is a pupil of the sculptor Arthur Lee.

Louis D. Brandeis   42.184

Head of Louis D. Brandeis (1856–1941), lawyer and Associate Justice of the United States Supreme Court (1916–1939).

Bronze, height 16 in. Signed: Eleanor Platt Sc. Dated 1911. Copyrighted.

REPLICAS: Boston Museum of Fine Arts (bronze); Supreme Court Building, Washington (bronze).

REFERENCE: E. J. Hipkiss, *Boston Museum of Fine Arts Bull.*, 41 (1943):2, ill.

GIFT OF CHARLES C. BURLINGHAM, BERNARD FLEXNER, AND THOMAS D. THACHER, 1942.

Charles Umlauf

1911–

BORN in South Haven, Michigan. Umlauf studied at the Art Institute of Chicago and the Chicago School of Sculpture. He is a member of the Sculptors Guild.

Horse   55.180

Made in 1953.

Stoneware, height 23¾ in.

EXHIBITED: Valley House, Dallas, Texas, 1953; Denver Art Museum, Colorado, 1954; Passedoit Gallery, New York, 1955.

PURCHASE, FLETCHER FUND, 1955.

Grace Turnbull

BORN in Baltimore, Maryland. Grace Turnbull studied art in Baltimore at the Maryland Institute.

Python of India   42.179

Westfield green marble, height 8 in. Signed: Turnbull. Dated 1941.

EXHIBITED: Baltimore Museum of Art, 1942; Metropolitan Museum, *Artists for Victory*, 1942, purchase prize.

PURCHASE, ROGERS FUND, 1942.

Irene Hamar

1912–

BORN in Brazil. Irene Hamar studied sculpture in Paris.

Meditation—Head of a Woman

42.112

Made about 1940.

Marble, height 13½ in. Signed: Irene Hamar.

GIFT OF DR. DANTON COELHO, 1942.

Herzl Emanuel

1914–

BORN in Scranton, Pennsylvania. When Emanuel was a high-school student in Rochester, New York, he began to attend classes in art at the Rochester Memorial Art Gallery. In 1931 he went to Paris, where he studied with Despiau at the Académie Scandinave and with Robert Wlerick at the Académie Grande Chaumière. Later he worked with Ossip Zadkine in Paris.

56.106

Savage Head 43·45·1

An imaginary portrait in the cubist style.

Painted plaster, height 19 in. Signed: H. Emanuel. Dated 1939.

Gift of the Works Progress Administration, New York City Art Project, 1943.

Spain 43.45.2

A seated woman in the cubist style, based on photographs of refugees during the Spanish Civil War.

Bronze, height 17⅝ in. Inscribed: N.Y.C. W.P.A. Art Project #938 [1938?].

Gift of the Works Progress Administration, New York City Art Project, 1943.

Richard Lippold

1915–

Born in Milwaukee, Wisconsin. Lippold studied at the Art Institute of Chicago and the University of Chicago.

Variation within a Sphere, No. 10: The Sun 56.106

An abstract construction commissioned by the Metropolitan Museum in 1953 and made between 1953 and 1956.

Gold-filled wire, 22 k., height 132 in., width 264 in.

References: L. Campbell, "Lippold Makes a Construction," *Art News*, 55 (Oct. 1956):30, ill.; H. Kramer, *Arts*, 31 (Oct. 1956):50, ill.; R. Lippold, "How to Make a Sculpture," *Art in America*, 44 (Winter, 1956):27, ill.; R. B. Hale, *Met. Mus. Bull.*, new series 16 (1957):28, ill.; F. C. Legrand, "La peinture et la sculpture au défi," *Quadrum*, 7 (1959):23, ill.; R. Lippold, "To Make Love to Life," *College Art Journal*, 19 (Summer, 1960):298, ill.

Purchase, Fletcher Fund, 1956.

55.183

Nathaniel Kaz

1917–

Born in New York. Kaz studied at the Art Students League under George Bridgman. He is a member of the Sculptors Guild, the Woodstock Society of Art, and the Brooklyn Society of Art.

Danse Espagnole 55.183

A group of dancers, cast in 1955.

Bronze, height 45⅛ in. Signed: Nathaniel Kaz. Dated 1952. Copyrighted; founder's mark: Roman Bronze Works, Corona, L.I. N.Y.

Exhibited: Pennsylvania Academy of the Fine Arts, Philadelphia, 1953; Whitney Museum of American Art, New York, 1953; American Museum of Natural History, New York, *Sculptors Guild Exhibition*, 1954.

Gift of Mr. and Mrs. William Peyton Marin, 1955.

42.182

William W. Swallow

1921-

BORN in Clark's Green, Pennsylvania. Swallow studied at the Philadelphia Museum's School of Industrial Art.

As the Earth Sings—Pennsylvania Dutch Family   42.182

Made in 1942.

Terra cotta, height 18 in. Signed: W W S (monogram).

REFERENCE: *Artists for Victory* (a picture book of the prize winners, Metropolitan Museum, 1942).

EXHIBITED: Metropolitan Museum, *Artists for Victory*, 1942, purchase prize.

PURCHASE, ROGERS FUND, 1942.

Index

Designed by Peter Oldenburg. Printed by Plantin Press in Monotype Granjon, on Warren Lustrogloss paper. Bound by Russell-Rutter Co.

First printing, April 1965, 3500 copies.
Second printing, November 1965, 2500 copies.
Third printing, May 1969, 2500 copies.